Fit to Dance?

About the authors

Dr Peter Brinson was awarded honorary degrees by three universities for his work in the study of dance and in making dance accessible. In 1964 he founded the Royal Ballet's Ballet for All company to present classical ballet of high quality on stages and in places larger companies could not reach. In 1972 he was appointed Director of the Calouste Gulbenkian Foundation (UK) and gave major assistance for the next 11 years to British dance, dance education and community arts. 'For achievements in dance' he received a London Dance and Performance Special Award in 1989 and the prestigious Digital Premier Award in 1992.

Fiona Dick worked for 10 years as co-Director of Dance Umbrella, the dance festival promoter and artist management service. Since turning freelance in 1990 she has undertaken a number of projects for national arts funding bodies and dance organisations and is currently Coordinator of Dance UK's *Healthier Dancer Programme.*

Fit to Dance?

THE REPORT OF THE NATIONAL INQUIRY INTO
DANCERS' HEALTH AND INJURY

BY
DR. PETER BRINSON
AND
FIONA DICK

Calouste Gulbenkian Foundation, London 1996

This report and related research has been administered and part
funded by Dance UK as part of its Healthier Dancer Programme.

Published by the
Calouste Gulbenkian Foundation
United Kingdom Branch
98 Portland Place
London W1B 1ET
Tel: 020 7908 7604
Email: info@gulbenkian.org.uk
Website: www.gulbenkian.org.uk

The right of Peter Brinson and Fiona Dick to be identified as
the authors of this work has been asserted in accordance with the
Copyright, Designs and Patents Act 1988.

ISBN 0 903319 70 5
ISBN (13) 9780 903319 70 6

British Library Cataloguing-in-Publication Data
A catalogue record for this book is available from the British Library

Designed by Chris Hyde
Reprinted by Lightning Source UK Ltd, MK13 8PR

Distributed by Central Books, 99 Wallis Road, London E9 5LN
Tel: 0845 458 9911, Fax: 0845 458 9912
Email: orders@centralbooks.com
Website: www.centralbooks.com

Front cover
Dancers: Kate Coyne, Rambert Dance Company
Darshan Singh Bhuller, Richard Alston Dance Company
Photograph: Anthony Crickmay

CONTENTS

DEDICATION

The contribution which Peter Brinson, a former Director of the Gulbenkian Foundation UK, made to the world of dance was outstanding. This report, on which Peter continued to work during his last months, is a fitting memorial to a remarkable person, as well as an important contribution to the causes he believed in.

Ben Whitaker
Director
Calouste Gulbenkian Foundation UK branch
July 1996

Dancers: Darshan Singh Bhuller/Andrew Robinson: London Contemporary Dance Theatre
Photograph: Anthony Crickmay

FOREWORD

Dance UK was formed in 1982 in response to a demand from many parts of the dance profession to find a unified voice. Its mission includes making the case for dance through lobbying, campaigning and advocacy, but also working towards the long-term advancement of dance through an ongoing programme of activities. Through the publication of this book Dance UK is both reaching out beyond dance to make a case for better support for the health of dancers, and motivating and encouraging those in dance to participate in this endeavour.

The health of dancers has long been a central concern for Dance UK. This concern was addressed through the Medical Advisory Panel (1986-1990) and through conferences such as *The Healthier Dancer* (1990), *Training Tomorrow's Professional Dancers* (1993) and *Fit to Dance?* (1995). There have also been a series of posters and a number of information sheets, as well as a Medical Register and a succession of Roadshows, all designed to disseminate information on health and fitness for dance.

This book is nonetheless a unique milestone in Dance UK's efforts. Its inception was the result of a 1992 Digital Dance Premier Award which was made to Peter Brinson. He culminated his remarkable contribution to dance by laying the foundations of this study; this investigation was close to his heart and he was working upon it in the last few weeks before his death, his briefcase at his bedside. Fortunately Fiona Dick, who was assisting Peter, was able to take up the work and has progressed it to the point of publication as co-writer and editor.

This book contains some findings which serve to challenge the traditional training and practices of the professional dance world. It is clear that there is far too much injury in dance today and that much of it may well be preventable. Equally it is clear that dancers are not as physically and psychologically prepared for the demands of their chosen path as they should be. To some extent, the two aspects go hand in hand. Everyone who cares about dance can and should help. Dancers must learn to take responsibility for themselves, even if their previous dance training has not always encouraged this. Companies have a duty of care to their employees which needs to be carefully considered in the light of these findings. Teachers and schools may face the greatest challenge, not only to reform their students, but to re-evaluate past practices, questioning each aspect in the light of new knowledge. The importance of the dance teacher cannot be overstated. Qualifications for dance teachers may need thorough deliberation; the current situation, in which literally anyone can hire a studio and accept students, does not reflect well upon a rigorous profession. There is also a growing recognition that the training of dance teachers is vital to the health of dance and dancers. Past experience as a dancer, no matter how accomplished, may not provide a guarantee of good teaching and the 'how' of teaching deserves as much attention as 'what' is being taught. In this respect parents have an important role to play and the informed choice of dance teacher may be crucial to the future of the dancer.

Finally, all of us who watch dance must be aware of the consequences of our aesthetic demands, whether it be for athletic sequences, for unnaturally idealised versions of slimness and youth, or for a constant diet of novel movement which explores the limits of human capability.

While this study challenges virtually all who are involved in dance, we must also acknowledge the important contribution that has been made to the work by many people who are working in dance today. The writing of reports such as this involves numerous people and while it is not possible to list everyone here, we must extend thanks to at least some of those who have contributed. Thanks are due to the members of the Editorial Board, who have made themselves available to Peter and to Fiona throughout the preparation of the book, and to the Dance UK Working Group who have devised strategies for implementing and disseminating the findings. All of these people have given freely of their time and are committed to carrying on the work in future. Thanks also to the Laban Centre for Movement and Dance for supporting the investigation into the psychological problems of dancers by accommodating the researchers and by providing them with secretarial support.

Special thanks to the Arts Council of England for finding money to complete the research when it needed more time than had originally been anticipated; to Anthony Crickmay for generously donating the use of his photographs; to the Contemporary Dance Trust for hosting the many meetings; to the library staff at the National Sports Medicine Institute and the National Resource Centre for Dance at the University of Surrey for their patient retrieval of articles and papers. Thanks also to the many dancers and dance students who took the time to complete questionnaires, the volunteers who agreed to be assessed (especially the dancers of Phoenix Dance Company); to the many researchers who generously allowed their findings to be incorporated before publication of their own more detailed accounts; to all the busy people who agreed to be interviewed and whose voices and views inform the findings of this study. Our overseas friends also provided support and advice, particularly the Harkness Center for Dance Injuries in New York, the Dancer Transition Resource Centre in Toronto, Tony Geeves in Australia and Eva Ramel in Sweden.

Once again it should be noted that this all began through the generosity of the Digital Equipment Company, whose Dance Awards supported over 70 new dance productions. However, the award to Peter Brinson, which made this report possible, may prove to be the most enduring contribution of all to the development of dance in Britain.

We should also make special note of the important role which the Calouste Gulbenkian Foundation has played throughout. It is entirely fitting that Peter Brinson's long association with the Foundation should have culminated in this publication, as it thoroughly demonstrates the commitment to positive change which was so important to Peter and has long been a hallmark of the Gulbenkian.

Peter realised that significant progress will be made only through the combined efforts of the dance profession, the funding bodies, the healthcare professionals and, most importantly, persuasive advocates. Peter's vision signposted the way; we at Dance UK hope that this book is a worthy tribute to his vision and an effective agent for change in the future he envisaged.

Christopher Bannerman
Chair
Dance UK

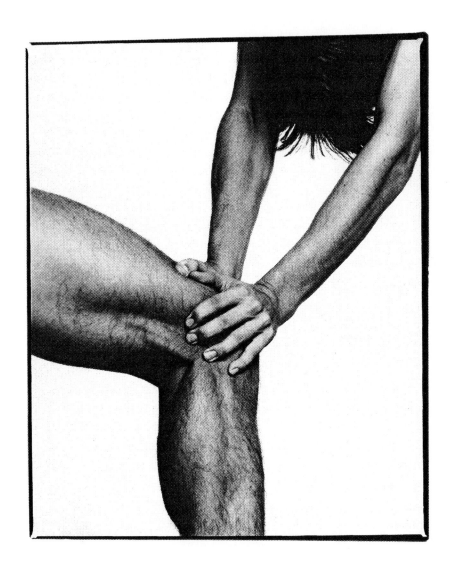

Dancers: Mathew Hart/Mathew Dibble: The Royal Ballet
Photograph: Anthony Crickmay

INTRODUCTION

Significance of dance

Dancers are artists who are athletes. And athletes who are artists. What they dance and how they dance has been part of the history of human movement, human culture and human communication since humanity began. That is the significance of dance. As a demanding form of human movement, dance increases knowledge of what the human body can achieve under stress. As an art form dance enriches our culture through expressive communication. As fun and recreation on stage, in the dance hall or club, dance makes an important contribution to enjoyment as well as to national fitness. Dance enhances the quality of life.

Wide range of dance careers

The people to whose need we call attention are mostly young, in their 20s and 30s. They are found in many more enterprises than the high-profile classical and contemporary dance companies which attract media attention in large theatres. They are the heart of smaller dance companies. They animate much commercial theatre, film and television, clubs and cabaret, cruise liners and circuses. They reveal through dance the cultures of Asia, Africa, the Caribbean and other parts of the world. They are professional ballroom dancers with a large following. They are independent freelance dancers travelling the world. They are choreographers inventing movement. They are dance notators and dance movement therapists. They work in community situations throughout Britain. They teach in dance companies, vocational institutions, schools, universities and recreation centres. They may become dance administrators, writers, historians or researchers. Together they are the dance profession of the United Kingdom, in number about 25,000 people.[1]

Lifestyles

Behind each dancer lies long training, for the female dancer often from the age of seven or eight, for the male normally from fourteen. Then each is selected by audition from numbers always greater than the jobs available. Ahead lie 20 or so years of dedicated hard work, applause, perhaps fame. Each day begins early and ends around midnight or later. Whatever the day's tasks, there is usually first the ritual of 'class' - a training session given by a teacher and taken by every dancer from the most famous to the beginner. For dancers day-long rehearsals follow. For teachers there are more classes to give. Dancers and teachers are affected by the work of choreographers creating or arranging dance and new movements. It is through intelligent exercise in daily class that dancers' bodies are prepared for choreographic demands. Stage and dance studios are laboratories; their end result the performance. During performance the movement of dancers combines with music, colour and the excitement of physical risk to create spectacle and drama. Or there might be no spectacle, no scenery, even no music - just one dancer dancing. It is still performance and communication.

Treatment of injury

If the dancer is injured, there is no dance. Injuries happen because dance is a high-risk business, like all athletic endeavour. In common with many sports, the physical demands made today are much greater than they were 30 years ago. When injuries happen, performances are spoiled, audiences disappointed, careers imperilled. Yet there is no specific national health provision for dancers to mitigate this risk. We need such provision in the public interest as well as in the interest of dancers. At the same time we do not wish to place dancers ahead of others injured or sick. Rather we argue for special arrangements which take account of dancers' unique work, their need to return quickly to performance and the benefits which dance brings to society as a whole. Such arrangements will cost money, requiring political will and public agreement. Therefore, this report is addressed to politicians and the general public as well as to the medical and dance professions.

Long-term aims

We set out on this work with several long-term aims, to:
- prevent or reduce dancers' injuries and illness
- safeguard and prolong dancers' careers, by enhancing their physical and artistic abilities
- benefit personal and dance company budgets through savings from improvements in dancers' health
- inform the medical and sports science professions of the special health, injury and fitness needs of dancers.

Results

Our findings form the essence of this report. We conclude that the absence of a special national health and injury service for dancers leads to low morale and a feeling of oppression among dancers. There are unnecessary days lost from work, forced early retirements, unanticipated changes of career, increased claims on state benefits.

How possible is change? The implications are wide-ranging for dancers and dance managements, the medical profession, dance schools, health educators and, ultimately, for Government and its Arts Councils.

References
1 *Careers and Training in Dance and Drama* (Institute of Manpower Studies, University of Sussex, 1994)

Dancers: Mathew Hart/Mathew Dibble: The Royal Ballet
Photograph: Anthony Crickmay

1
The problem

THE PROBLEM

Causes and effects of injury

In November 1992 Dance UK, the national organisation for dance professionals, published *A Dancer's Charter.* The charter drew on the opinions of many professional dancers and dance teachers in conference. Injury, said the dancers, is often due to overwork, to the demands of choreographers seeking to manipulate limbs and bodies in new ways, to excessive rehearsals, poor teaching especially when young, bad planning by dance staff or management, cold theatres and unsprung floors; and sometimes the lifestyles of dancers themselves, including poor eating habits. Some of these causes are already being addressed by the dance profession. Some are the result of inadequate funding. Nevertheless, dance is a risk business, like sport. Notwithstanding the best arrangements, injuries will occur. The result can be disastrous not only for a company's performance, budget and box-office income, but also for other dancers called to extra rehearsals, resulting in overwork for those other dancers, and above all for the career of an injured dancer. In that crisis the needs of the dance profession may conflict with the philosophy and current practice of the National Health Service.

The National Health Service

The philosophy of the National Health Service is to sustain the general health of the nation. 'Why' runs the argument, 'should we devote time and resources away from treating the elderly or young families or people doing their daily jobs in order to treat injuries to the young and fit? These injuries are derived from voluntary choice and therefore self-inflicted.' However, those who exercise diminish the risk of a range of other expensive medical conditions. It is now officially recognised that fitness is an important aspect of general health. Dancers certainly exercise. And like all people who do a lot of exercise, they are sometimes injured. Moreover, dance is also a way of earning a living like any other occupation open to young people. Therefore it should receive similar attention in health care. **A dance injury is a work-related injury.** When it occurs, the greatest need of the injured dancer - and of the company to which he or she belongs - is instant treatment. This is not only to repair the damage but to return the dancer to performance and earning capacity as soon as possible. In its accident and emergency provision the NHS is without peer. Most dance injuries, however, begin more slowly. There are symptoms, usually pain, which the dancer hopes will go away. Finally he or she visits a general practitioner. Under NHS procedures, this must be done in order to reach specialist services.

CASE HISTORY 1

'L' started working in contemporary dance and has now moved into physical theatre. His only injury in a long career as a dancer was when working with a guest choreographer in a style for which he had no previous training. Years later he was directing a demanding course and not sufficiently warming up before class because of the other responsibilities involved. He ignored some small niggles in his right leg. On the last day he was doing jumps in class when there was a distinct popping noise. He went to Casualty at the local hospital, where the injury was diagnosed as 'a tear' and he was given some physiotherapy. Back home his local hospital continued with physiotherapy but there was no improvement. After five weeks he decided to pay for private treatment and the injury was finally properly diagnosed as a ruptured Achilles tendon. The recommended operation would have cost several thousand pounds if done privately, money 'L' did not have, so he opted for the NHS. The surgeon encased the leg in heavy plaster after the operation and told 'L' to keep it on for three months. As a consequence, all the muscles in his leg became weak and he is still having problems with his ankle.

'When I talked to dancers in Holland I discovered that the normal time there to keep plaster on after an Achilles rupture is two weeks, not three months. Next time I have anything wrong, I'll try to make sure to be in Holland!'

Gap between NHS and dance profession

Members of the medical profession as a whole, and general practitioners in particular, have little experience of the physiological and psychological stresses which accompany intensive physical activity, including dance. Therefore GPs, with rare exceptions, lack the experience to diagnose or treat dance or sports injuries, many of which have become chronic; chronic injuries require a different approach from acute injuries. In addition, some injuries are seen only in dancers because of the particular demands of their work. Men have very specific lower back problems because of the demands of lifting their partners and carrying them around the stage. Women have stress fractures in the lower leg, arthritis in hips and toes, damaged knees. Not understanding dancers' professional lifestyles and healthcare needs, GPs may not realise, for example, that a dance patient must remain active while recuperating, without returning to full work. This implies treatment different from that offered to non-dancer patients with similar problems. In some cases, under the new funding arrangements, GPs are reluctant to give time and money to such special cases.

Response of large dance companies

Large dance companies and commercial managements have responded to this complexity with their own arrangements, assembling in slightly different ways their own groups of doctors, physiotherapists and specialists in dancers' health needs. So too have larger dance schools. This action has three results. First, dance companies and schools receive expert immediate treatment appropriate to the problem. Second, insurance provision means that dancers or students rarely pay the full cost of treatment, although they may have to contribute. Third, the arrangements provide models for wider application within the dance profession.

Need for special dancers' service

This wider application should embrace the majority of professional dancers. It is they who at present must take their place in the NHS queue. Occasionally they may find there doctors and specialists who understand dance needs and stresses. More often disappointed, they will opt for private treatment. However, many dancers' earnings are very low. **Private treatment therefore represents an enormous financial burden**, resulting in personal stress, less money for food and further damage to the dancer's health and morale. Some other solution is needed. This solution might combine experience of the health arrangements of larger companies and dance schools, NHS practice, private treatment schemes and insurance services to create a national health and injury service for all professional dancers and vocational dance students. It should be free, or nearly free, to dancers, particularly for expensive treatment. It should offer advisory health services to companies and dancers. It should carry out health checks on dancers at the beginning of each season. It should run courses for dancers, dance teachers and managements on how to sustain health and prevent injury.

Sources of medical support

Where lies the medical experience which might help to create such a service? A number of private clinics and remedial exercise centres have developed to serve dancers during the last two decades. They involve sympathetic orthopaedic and rheumatological consultants, physiotherapists, osteopaths and other health practitioners. Many dancers and dance companies refer to Dance UK's Medical Register Helpline, especially when on tour. The British Performing Arts Medicine Trust (BPAMT) runs a similar helpline for all performing artists. The British Association of Sport and Medicine (BASM) has published a Register of Sports Injury and Physiotherapy Clinics throughout the UK, both private and NHS. A few units have been established within the NHS for dancers' and performing artists' injuries, living halfway between the National Health Service and private treatment, troubled by the demands of fundraising, marketing and business operation. Nevertheless the number of such clinics is growing.

Infancy of sports/dance medicine

The resources of medical experience do, therefore, exist. They remain scattered and uncoordinated because sports medicine, and even more so dance medicine, remain in their infancy. There are, for example, only limited centres for study. The courses are mainly for GPs and can include only limited clinical experience. There is too a flow of reports and articles in medical and scientific journals facilitating international exchange of knowledge and contacts. Much of this information is gathered in databases that can be consulted at the Centre for Sports Science and Sports History at University of Birmingham, the National Sports Medicine Institute in London, the National Coaching Foundation centre at Leeds Metropolitan University, and the National Resource Centre for Dance at the University of Surrey.

Need for coordination

The articles, reports and conferences, the meetings of many national bodies and the annual gatherings of the International Association for Dance Medicine and Science, all illustrate the positive spread of knowledge. They illustrate also its negative element: the fragmented nature of knowledge in all countries. The many organisations seeking to coordinate this provision are positive in intention but may also be part of the problem. There is the British Association of Sport and Medicine, the British Performing Arts Medicine Trust, the National Coaching Foundation, the British Association of Sport and Exercise Sciences, the British Olympic Association, the National Sports Medicine Institute, the Sports Councils and many others. In the UK there is a need for centres which look not only at sports and dance injuries but at the whole area of dance and sports medicine and science. Injury, fitness, performance enhancement, choreographic and teaching practice, rehabilitation, nutrition, use of equipment, shoes, psychological issues and research form a comprehensive area of dance need. This links the dance and medical professions. It is the plan of the Government and the Sports Councils that the new British Academy of Sport will pull together today's disparate provision into some sort of comprehensive service. Until such a service exists dancers must work towards their own provision.

Contribution to national fitness

A national health and injury service for dancers could actually assist the development of a comprehensive service by drawing together existing experience of dance needs in both private and public health care. Such a service would aim to take advantage of existing knowledge, expertise and resources in order to target the specific needs of dancers. The knowledge thus gained would have national value outside the dance profession. It would contribute to the development of national fitness emphasised in the Government's Green Paper *The Health of the Nation*[1] and the Allied Dunbar *National Fitness Survey.*[2] Such knowledge should be applied on a wider scale to the many thousands in the UK who look to dance for recreation, amateur performance, social enjoyment or education. At present the knowledge locked in professional dance experience remains mostly unexplored by medical services.

Value of professional experience

In indicating the contribution dance can make to national fitness, we have not claimed more for it than can be claimed for any sport. However, dance also includes a unique expressive content which should not be neglected. Top dancers, among whom are leading ballroom dancers, are enormously important for their example. Stimulating people to activity, dance can help reduce coronary heart disease, raise national fitness levels and save significant sums in the National Health budget. The National Fitness Survey refers only to social dancing, presumably embracing ballroom, disco and folk. These forms of dance, with their allies Keep Fit and aerobics, are among the top 20 most frequently mentioned recreational and competitive activities. Dance in other forms is noted as a major growth area, especially for women. To this should be added the special application of professional dance knowledge. This embraces community projects by dance animateurs, dance education through the National Curriculum and dance for people with special needs through local and health authorities. Capable of application to different ages at different levels of intensity - light, moderate or vigorous - dance is important in the concept of national aerobic fitness because of the degree of physical exertion it demands over a significant time span. Dance could not contribute to a culture of national fitness for the general population without the experience of professional dance at the highest level. Dance can be seen as an athletic activity and so should benefit from the same support services that the State provides for sports.

A political case

Alongside the case for a dancers' national health and injury service emerges also, therefore, a political case. **Such a national service would be in the national interest because what benefits dancers in health care, fitness and additional knowledge around particular injuries ultimately benefits the general population.** Dancers contribute to the quality of life of this population. They contribute to the national economy not only through performances, festivals, tourism, overseas earnings, employment and educational opportunities, but also through attracting overseas students to their leading schools. Such a significant contribution cannot be sustained except by dancers fit and free from injury.

Political and medical responses

It follows that a health and injury service for dancers requires a political response as well as a medical and scientific response. The political response at national and local level needs to be reflected in support for clinics and trained people as well as funding. The medical and scientific response requires changes of attitude touched upon already:

- recognition that dance injuries, like sports injuries, need particular understanding by the medical profession
- therefore greater knowledge in the medical profession of the lifestyles and healthcare needs of professional dancers in training and performance
- redressing neglect of dancers in healthcare provision
- closer liaison between the dance and medical professions
- stronger links between sports medicine/sports science and the dance profession to assist in prevention of dance injuries and in development of dance medicine and science, especially in the area of healthcare provision
- in-service courses for medical and primary care services in the healthcare needs of professional dancers
- more research into the nature, causes and frequency of professional dance injuries and health problems.

To these needs we address ourselves in the following chapters.

References
1 *The Health of the Nation: a strategy for health in England,* (HMSO, 1992)
2 Activity and Health Research, *Allied Dunbar National Fitness Survey: a report on activity patterns and fitness levels. Main findings,* (Sports Council and Health Education Authority, 1992)

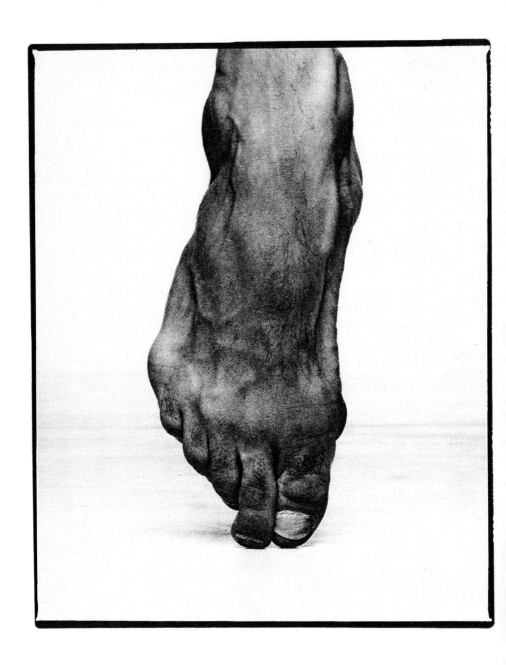

Dancer: Dimitri Gruzdyev: English National Ballet
Photograph: Anthony Crickmay

2
Methodology

METHODOLOGY

Initiation of research
In the previous chapter we established a need to explore dancers' health and injuries. There is as yet not enough knowledge from which to devise a positive health and injuries policy for all dancers, although larger dance companies have policies which can serve as models. Therefore we have launched the comprehensive research described in this chapter.

Objectives
We undertook this research with several objectives, to:
- focus professional expertise on dancers' health and injury needs, drawing on medical, dance and sports science resources
- understand better the role of physical fitness and counselling in reducing injury, illness and psychological problems
- demonstrate to the dance profession the need to reform creative practices, teaching practices and dancers' life styles in the interest of dancers' health.

Evidence available
Much of the evidence needed to establish a base of knowledge has been available for a long time. It lies in the actual performance of dancers on stage and in the records of dance companies. It is to be found in the experience of orthopaedic surgeons, physiotherapists, osteopaths, other health practitioners and dance teachers. It has been discussed and assessed in medical papers presented to national and international conferences. Generally speaking, the evidence is compelling that dancers need a new deal to face and overcome the undoubted risks of their profession.

Principal sources
We needed first to establish the different patterns of injury and health risks in different forms of dance employment and practice. Our sources for this lie in two principal areas. First, in dance companies, groups and dance schools of every size, the majority of whom are members of Dance UK or the Council for Dance Education and Training. Second, among members and organisations of the medical profession and sports science concerned with dancers' health and injuries. Those we have consulted,

either in person or by post, are listed in Appendix D.

Dance sources

Our dance sources comprise professional dancers and managements in large and small subsidised classical ballet companies, contemporary dance companies and in commercial theatre. Throughout Britain there also exists a network of smaller professional dance companies, dance groups and independent dance performers. Among them are artists from the dance cultures and styles of the former British Empire, now a valuable part of British dance culture. Therefore the South Asian Shobana Jeyasingh Dance Company, the pan-African Adzido Dance Company and the Afro-Caribbean Irie! companies are among our sources. So too are individual independent dancers like Siobhan O'Neill and Gill Clarke. We have consulted also the many schools and their students who supply these dance sources with trained dancers.

Medical and sports science sources

In the medical and sports science fields we have consulted orthopaedic surgeons, physicians, physiotherapists, osteopaths, nutritionists, body conditioning teachers and other specialists and sports scientists. Some are attached to dance companies, many are independent. Some work within the NHS, others privately. We have looked for help also to the leading organisations of sports medicine and sports science, such as the Sports Council and the National Sports Medicine Institute. Other organisations have a more specific remit, such as the Crystal Palace Sports Injury Centre and the British Performing Arts Medicine Trust. We have sought evidence abroad by attending the annual meetings of the International Association for Dance Medicine and Science (IADMS) and by developing links made there. We have drawn on much written evidence in national medical journals across the world. References are given at the end of each chapter.

Qualifying factors

As we drew on these sources, it became clear that there were a number of qualifying factors affecting our research. Opinions vary, for example, on the level of fitness and strength currently deriving from dance training and how this might relate to dance health and injury. Differences exist not only between one dance style and another but between dance and other forms of athletic activity. Some of these differences are considered in chapter 4. There are levels of psychological stress deriving from dance performance and dance training which need to be considered for their contribution to injury and health problems. These stresses are considered in chapter 5. There is a general need to take into account the actual health and fitness of dancers, male and female, as the base from which to undertake research and make judgements.

Questions to be answered

These qualifying factors and our discussions with dance, medical and sports science sources have guided what we needed to describe and question as we proceeded through our research. What is the habitual physical activity of dancers in different dance forms and the effectiveness of their daily training in developing strength and stamina? What is the relationship between this activity and the potential for preventing injury and ill-health? How do the personal life styles of dancers and company life styles affect this potential? What psychological stress factors are involved? And what is the significance of diet, rest and environmental factors? Discovering answers to these questions provides the programme of our work and the final question. What policies and strategies should be pursued by Government and its agencies, dance managements, dancers, dance teachers and the medical profession to reduce injury risks, improve dancers' fitness and diminish the economic, career and artistic costs of absence from work due to injury and ill health?

Structure of the inquiry

The inquiry's overall policy was guided by the Editorial Board listed at the beginning of this report. The project was originally chaired by the late Dr Peter Brinson and coordinated throughout by Fiona Dick, arts consultant. Dance UK provided an administrative base and received regular reports. Detailed research was undertaken by a Research Team, also chaired by Peter Brinson, coordinated by Fiona Dick and comprising:

CASE HISTORY 2

'N' was one of the best students at her school, and was confident of landing a good job, but when she started going to auditions she realised just how many good dancers were around. Several times she made it to the last few candidates but her lack of experience told against her. She did two projects with young choreographers, but they only paid expenses, so when the opportunity of ten months' work overseas came up, she jumped at it.

The letter of intent was fairly vague and when the dancers arrived they had to start negotiating a more specific contract with the management. Meanwhile rehearsals began for a piece which involved a lot of running around. After two months 'N' started getting pain in the left knee. The company could not recommend a physiotherapist, suggesting a plastic surgeon instead. He took X-rays but could see only severe inflammation, and suggested an injection. When she demurred, he prescribed anti-inflammatory pills which made her feel sick. The pain was still getting worse, so she decided to return to Britain for a second opinion. The management pressured her not to go but in the end relented, giving her a week to sort it out.

In London a dance-experienced therapist suspected a stress fracture and advised complete rest while waiting for the results of X-rays. It transpired that a spur had snapped off and was lodged round the back of the Achilles tendon, blocking movement into the foot; surgery would be necessary. Fortunately 'N' had thought to take out private medical insurance before going abroad so all these costs were covered. When she told the company they said they had already taken on a replacement and her contract was finished. It then took her several months, and the involvement of lawyers, to recover the money that was owed to her.

The operation went well, and while recuperating she took a Dance UK course on water fitness. She spent the whole of the next week in the pool and by the end could really feel the difference. She decided to train as a water fitness tutor and is now also studying to become an exercise therapist in order to help other independent dancers to make a full recovery from injury.

- for research into the current levels of fitness and possible prevention of dance injuries and ill-health: **Dr Yiannis Koutedakis**, senior lecturer in exercise physiology at the University of Wolverhampton
- for research into the nutritional status of dancers and suggestions for improvement: **Dr Paul Pacy,** formerly of the Nutrition Research Unit at St Pancras Hospital, London and currently in the Unit of Metabolic Medicine at St Mary's Hospital, Paddington, together with **Magita Khalouha**, PhD student
- for research into the causes and reduction of dance stresses and related problems: **Angelica Herold MacArthur,** dance clinical psychologist and **Matthew Wyon**, independent lecturer and physiologist, both working from facilities kindly provided by the Laban Centre for Movement and Dance
- for research among individual dancers, dance directors, choreographers and dance managers; surgeons, physiotherapists, other medical specialists and general practitioners; medical, sports science and dance organisations: **Fiona Dick**, supported by **Peter Brinson.**

Background surveys

The problem is long-standing. An editorial in *The Lancet* in 1985 stated that 'Injury is the most frequent medical problem among dancers of classical ballet and modern dance.' At the beginning of our research we inherited the results of important surveys into dancers' health and injuries in Australia and the UK. Reported during 1990, a survey by Dr Ann Bowling and Patricia Sohl drew on results of research in the USA, Australia, the UK, Denmark and Russia. This established the frequency of chronic injury, the locations of injury and the causes, diagnosis and treatment. More detailed surveys in 1988/89 of classical and modern dancers in the UK by Ann Bowling for Dance UK and in Australia by Tony Geeves for what is now Ausdance confirmed the seriousness of the situation in both countries. Around half of dancers surveyed in the UK and two-thirds in Australia reported chronic injuries affecting their dancing, often sustained early in their careers. These findings were reported to Dance UK's 1990 conference on *The Healthier Dancer*, much of which was developed further by Dance UK's 1993 conference on *Training Tomorrow's Professional Dancers*. The reports of these conferences have provided important source material.[1,2]

Other evidence

We inherited also the results of an investigation into upper body strength in male Birmingham Royal Ballet dancers described by Dr Yiannis Koutedakis at the 1993 conference. We had access to the records of some dance companies and of some injury clinics. During the two years of research, the Editorial Board saw approximately 250 performances of professional dance of all kinds, at all levels and in many different conditions, in order to remain well informed about the state of British dance and new choreography.

Procedure

Early on, the Editorial Board agreed a procedure of investigation in five stages:

- a survey by questionnaire of individual professional dancers. This was drafted in consultation with the Editorial Board, Dr Ann Bowling and several individual dancers, then distributed by Dance UK before analysis by Dr Yiannis Koutedakis at the University of Wolverhampton
- a survey by questionnaire of professional dance managements. This was drafted in consultation with the Editorial Board, Dr Ann Bowling and several company managers. It was again distributed by Dance UK and then analysed by Fiona Dick and Dr Ann Bowling
- supplementary visits to dance companies and individual dancers
- investigation into present medical provision in the field of dancers' health, including comparison with the sports medicine field for lessons to be learned
- research into fitness and nutrition, conducted on 50 volunteer dancers by Dr Yiannis Koutedakis in Wolverhampton and London and by Dr Paul Pacy in London.

Parallel inquiries

As the project developed, supplements were added to these stages. A survey of injuries among dancers in musical theatre conducted by Caroline Kitchin was reported in *Dancing Times* and made available to us in detail. Phoenix Dance Company launched a separate project with Yiannis Koutedakis which looked at appropriate forms of training. The investigation into dancers' health was supplemented by research into the psychological aspects of dance performance and training by Angelica Herold MacArthur with help from Matthew Wyon and the Laban Centre for Movement and Dance. Finally, of course, we supplemented this detailed research by conference visits and a literature review of available medical papers, studies, books and reports.

Summary

Our two-year research has therefore focused on professional dancers in companies, approached through questionnaires and interviews. We reached company managements in the same way. We reached the medical profession primarily by personal contact and interview and consulted also counsellors concerned with both the physical and the personal stresses of professional dancing. This focus included dancers and managements in commercial theatre as well as subsidised companies. It included research into stress and ill health as well as physical injury. It bore in mind always the idea that prevention of injury and ill health is preferable, being cheaper and safer than the need for treatment.

References
1 *The Healthier Dancer*, Laban Centre for Movement and Dance (London, 1991, reprinted 1995)
2 *Tomorrow's Dancers*, Laban Centre for Movement and Dance (London, 1994)

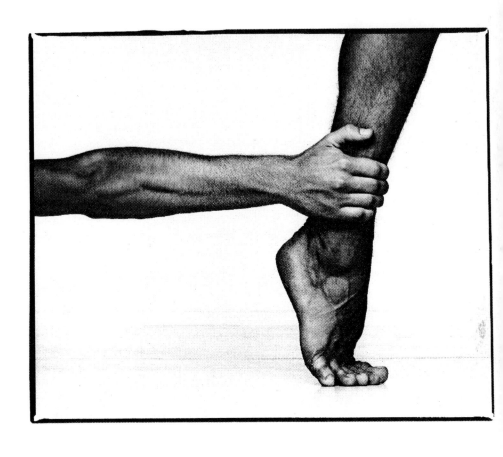

Dancers: Mathew Dibble/Mathew Hart: The Royal Ballet
Photograph: Anthony Crickmay

3
Results of the questionnaires

RESULTS OF THE QUESTIONNAIRES

Individual questionnaires

The questionnaire to individual dancers was designed to determine the incidence of dance-related injuries in the previous 12 months, establishing the causes as perceived by the dancers, the treatment obtained and associated costs. There were also a number of questions relating to the dancer's lifestyle - smoking, drinking, diet - and to the incidence of psychological problems such as stress, depression and low self-confidence. A copy of this questionnaire appears in Appendix A.

Problems of self-reporting

Obviously the accuracy of response depended upon the dancer's own recollection of the recent past, which is why the questions were limited to events in the previous year. No cross-checks with medical or other records were carried out since the respondents were assured of complete confidentiality. However, it is generally accepted that there is usually good agreement between self-reports and medical records when people are asked questions about the recent past and on subjects which are of particular concern or interest to them.

Definition of injury

There are several possible definitions of injury. For instance, other researchers have defined injuries as those requiring professional consultation, or involving insurance claims or other payment for treatment. However, it appears that dancers under-report injury, for a multiplicity of reasons. As an example, a Swedish study related that over a three-year period one company therapist treated 376 different new dance injuries, of which the dancers had officially reported only 40.[1] We therefore decided to rely upon the dancers' own perception of the injuries sustained and defined the term **injury** as 'a physical or psychological problem deriving from stress or other causes to do with performance, rehearsal, training, touring or the circumstances of dance life'.

Distribution of the individual questionnaires

The individual questionnaire was circulated to every dance company on the Arts Council of England's Green and White Lists.[2] It went also to dancers in South Asian dance from a list supplied by ADiTi (the national development agency for South Asian dance); to independent dancers in Scotland from a list supplied by Dance Productions and in Wales from an Arts Council of Wales list. Dance agencies such as Chisenhale Dance Space, the Holborn Centre for Performing Arts and the Brighton Dance Agency agreed to hand them out to any professional dancer attending the centre. Three hundred were distributed to dancers in musical theatre via the Society of London Theatre. At a later stage, as a result of Dance UK's international conference on training professional dancers, it was decided to include vocational students on courses accredited by the Council for Dance Education and Training. First-year students would have had only six weeks of full-time training at the time of survey, so were omitted in order to confine the scope to those who were subject to pressures similar to professional dancers. In all, 3,500 questionnaires were distributed.

Response rates

The total of 658 usable replies provides the largest response of British dancers and dance students ever achieved. All the replies have been entered onto a computer database and represent a valuable resource for further research. Nevertheless, the number of respondents is fairly low compared with the estimated overall British dance population. The most obvious bias problem is that people who have been injured will be more willing and interested to respond than those who are so far unscathed. While the responses obviously give some indication of the types and locations of injury, it is not possible to draw any conclusions about the frequency of injury in the overall British dance population. In particular, there was a very low response from South Asian (20) and Afro-Caribbean (11) dancers, so the present findings cannot be applied with any certainty to dancers working in these styles. Nevertheless, the findings appear sensible, in line with other injury surveys, as will be seen later, and were borne out by in-depth interviews with individual dancers.

Parallel management questionnaire

At the same time, a management questionnaire, reproduced in Appendix B, was sent to 54 companies employing dancers. The same definition of injury was used. Again, the Arts Council's Green and White Lists[2] provided the basic distribution list, with help from the Society of London Theatre to reach the five commercial managements. Forty-one, or 76%, responded and the replies were analysed by Ann Bowling and Fiona Dick.

Gender

Of the total sample of individual dancers, 500 (76%) were women and 158 (24%) men. This represents a higher proportion of women than in the original Bowling survey[3] but probably reflects accurately the gender balance in the dance profession as a whole. It is interesting to compare this with the generally accepted figure of 60% of men who regularly participate in sporting activities. Except where specifically noted, no significant differences were found between the sexes on any of the questions.

Age distribution

The age distribution was similar for both men and women:

Age	Men (%)	Women (%)	Total sample (%)
16-19	23 (15)	175 (35)	198 (30)
20-24	46 (29)	149 (30)	195 (30)
25-29	34 (22)	90 (18)	124 (19)
30-34	33 (21)	41 (8)	74 (11)
35-39	15 (10)	27 (6)	42 (7)
40-44	5 (3)	15 (3)	20 (3)

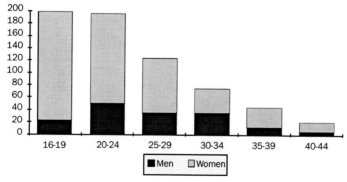

Distribution by age and gender

Occupation and training status

Fifty per cent of the respondents (330) were pre-professional students and fifty per cent professional dancers. This reflects the estimated 2,000 performers[4] and 2,200 students on accredited courses at any one time.[5] While the professional ballet dancers had trained for an average of six years, the other professionals had most commonly trained for three years. Both groups had on average been working for 10 years since training.

Dance style

Many of the students gave multiple answers to this question. This is probably because their training covers a number of different styles. The breakdown for the professionals, some of whom again worked in more than one style, is as follows:

Form	Number	% of professionals
Contemporary	209	64
Ballet	98	30
Jazz	19	6
South Asian	15	5
Tap	11	3
Afro-Caribbean	8	2
Other	62	19

'Other' included a variety of responses, such as 'new dance', 'physical theatre' and 'contact improvisation', and also musical theatre. The management survey showed that ballet companies between them employed only 380 dancers out of the estimated total of 2,000, or some 19%. The answers to the Healthier Dancer questionnaire are therefore somewhat weighted towards the ballet dancer working for one of the major companies.

Findings on injuries

Types of injuries in last year

It is as well to recall that by the term 'injuries' we are referring to those self-reported injuries sustained in a 12-month period prior to the

Type	Ballet professionals %	Contemporary professionals %	Other professionals %	Students %
Muscles	64	66	27	55
Joints	40	38	39	34
Skeleton/ bones	16	31	12	20
Other	11	10	12	17
None	17	16	37	17

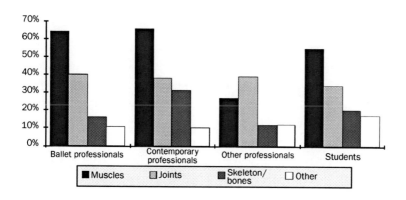

distribution of the questionnaire. Since 17% of ballet professionals reported no injuries, we can deduce that 83% in this survey sustained at least one injury, compared with 84% of the contemporary dancers and 83% of the students, a remarkably consistent finding. Some respondents ticked more than one category of injury incurred; in fact the ballet and contemporary professional dancers sustained three injuries each on average. It is interesting to note that dancers working in other styles reported fewer injuries, which may reflect the more intermittent workload or the better preventive practices of these dancers.

Frequency rates reported in other surveys: Britain
Ann Bowling's survey of British professional dancers in 1988 found that 84% of the 141 dancers investigated had suffered at least one injury at some time in their career that had affected their dancing. Moreover,

42% had been injured in the previous six months.[3] Caroline Kitchin found that 76% of the musical theatre dancers she surveyed had been injured seriously enough to affect their dancing at some point in their career.[6] In the British ballroom dancing sector, it has been reported that in 14 days of international competition there were 134 casualties, 10% of them necessitating hospital treatment.[7]

Other injury surveys: overseas

An American survey by Robert Stephens and Allan Ryan, in 1982/83, reported that more than 90% of professional ballet dancers in Ballet West and advanced student dancers from the summer programme had been injured at some time in their careers.[8] On Broadway, 56% of musical theatre performers surveyed by Randolph Evans et al were found to have been injured in the previous year.[9] In Sweden, Eva Ramel and Ulrich Moritz found that 95% of the professional ballet dancers working in companies had been injured over the same period of time, reporting more injuries than any other group of artists.[1] However, Australian professional dancers reported a 56% incidence of injury in the previous six months when surveyed by Tony Geeves in 1989.[10] From these and other surveys, it seems safe to conclude that most professional and pre-professional dancers will be injured at some time in their careers.

The size of the problem in sport

Dancers are not alone. A Sports Council survey in 1991 estimated that in England and Wales there were over 19 million exercise-related new injuries a year, more than half of them potentially serious. Of these, an estimated 1.4 million resulted in people having to take time off work, on average for six days, at an estimated indirect cost of £405 million. The authors estimated the direct treatment costs of these injuries at about £240 million, with recurrent injuries costing perhaps another £350 million.[11] In the opinion of some specialists this is the equivalent of an unrecognised epidemic, causing much more trouble than many of the better-recognised conditions.

Anatomical sites of injury

In line with some of the previously published data,[1,6,10] the lower back was the most common site of injury. For the ballet and other dancers

Type	Ballet professionals %	Contemporary professionals %	Other professionals %	Students %
Neck	23	30	26	11
Shoulders	15	22	23	8
Arms/hands	10	12	13	5
Upper back	11	24	19	7
Ribs	negligible	4	3	5
Lower back	47	48	42	42
Pelvis	15	16	16	16
Thighs	14	13	16	15
Lower legs	26	16	16	23
Knees	32	41	32	30
Ankles	42	29	42	30
Feet	33	23	19	21

Sites of injuries (all dancers)

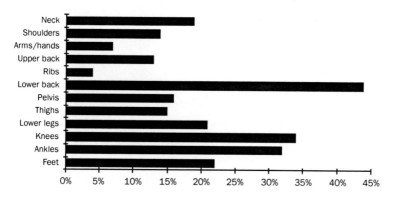

this was followed by ankles, feet, knees and lower legs, while for contemporary dancers the next most affected sites were knees, neck, ankle and upper back. The pattern differed between the sexes, with 42%

of males reporting injuries to the lower back compared with 34% of females. Rates for knees and ankles were very similar but thereafter females were most injured in the feet (18%) and lower legs (17%), while males were most injured in the shoulder (26%) and neck (23%), reflecting perhaps the greater amount of lifting that is required of the male dancer. Students reported fewer injuries than professionals to neck, shoulder and upper back, probably because they are not yet being required to take weight in the same way. In corroboration of these findings, respondents to the management survey gave the most frequent sites of injury as lower back, ankles, feet and knees.

Sites of injury in other styles
A small study was carried out for this report of ballroom dancers treated at the Crystal Palace Sports Injury Centre over the four years 1991/94. This showed that the major site of injury was the knee, followed by the lower back and the upper back or neck. Likewise, the Broadway performers were found to have most trouble with their knees, thereafter being equally likely to injure ankles, feet, neck or lower back.[9] It will be interesting to compare these findings with the survey of performers in London West End productions undertaken by the same team in late 1995.

Place of injury
The management study indicated that dancers are particularly vulnerable to injury during rehearsals, with a risk of injury twice as great than in performance and three and a half times more than in class. This is the same pattern as in Australia.[10] However, one commercial company presenting a long-run show, and therefore only calling rehearsals when required, reported a large number of injuries in performance (220 in one year). Caroline Kitchin's survey of musical theatre dancers found the risk of injury in rehearsals to be more than twice as great as the risks in class or performance.[6] Experience suggests that it is in rehearsal that dancers may be asked to do new things for which their bodies are not properly prepared.

Perceived causes
A number of interviewees complained about the inadequacy of early training in relation to injuries, especially in ballet. The teacher may

teach badly, the student learn poorly or try a completely new movement with inadequate preparation. Our own research, discussed more fully in chapter 4, finds a link between poor levels of fitness and number of injuries. The dancers themselves perceived the causes as a number of rather complex inter-related factors, often citing multiple causes for their injuries.

Perceived causes

Cause	Ballet professionals %	Contemporary professionals %	Other professionals %	Students %
Fatigue/ overwork	57	60	61	52
Unsuitable floor	47	37	16	1
Repetitive movements	38	45	23	19
Cold environment	37	36	29	1
Ignoring early warning signs	23	34	45	34
Insufficient warm up	15	25	16	21
Difficult choreography	14	29	13	9
Partnering work	12	18	3	9
Psychological	9	15	13	12
Different choreographers	7	6	negligible	1
Inadequate diet	4	9	13	8
Other	28	22	32	36

Dancers agreed that by far the major cause was fatigue/overwork. This was also the main reason given by the Swedish dancers.[1] Ballet dancers then cited unsuitable floors, while the other professional dancers were more concerned about cold spaces, repetitive movements and ignoring early warning signs. The musical theatre dancers suggested that warmer studios and theatres would be the most useful means of injury prevention.[6] However, the managers, when asked about factors for injury prevention, focused on the dancers' taking responsibility for their own bodies, citing the need for more education about such matters as warming up, proper stretching and care of the body. This difference in perspective between the dancers themselves and the managements needs further discussion in any consideration of a programme to promote health and prevent injury.

CASE HISTORY 3

'M' is a senior artist with a ballet company. He had severe shin splints during his first two years of vocational training, probably due to being a late developer and growing very quickly during this period. While dancing in the *corps* he was identified as promising and was pushed very hard. One show was particularly difficult, with a heavy costume and technically demanding fast work. An injury to another dancer meant that he had to do all the performances without any cover. Then someone else was injured and he had to learn their new part in another work from video, at the same time as rehearsing for a triple bill. His leg started aching and became steadily worse. Then in a matinee performance he felt the leg 'go'. The company physiotherapist suspected a stress fracture. However, he had to go on for the evening show because there was no cover. This aggravated the injury and he had to be off work for six months.

'Dancers are afraid of being seen as lazy or unworthy, they are afraid to go and talk to the management. Injuries should be seen as a positive opportunity to resolve the problem, not as purely negative.'

Reaction to warning signs of injury
From the table on perceived causes it can be seen that more than one-third of the dancers gave one of the causes of injury as ignoring early warning signs. In answer to a further question, 76% of the professional

dancers said they would take their own steps in reaction to warning signs and only 37% would seek professional treatment. It is possible that this is due to restricted access to suitable treatment, plus inability to afford the associated costs. It is interesting to note that in Caroline Kitchin's survey 88% of the injured musical theatre dancers sought professional advice or treatment.[6] It will be seen in chapter 7 that, for the most part, commercial managements have made arrangements for their dancers to consult appropriate professionals.

Treatment received

Contemporary and other dancers were as likely to consult an osteopath as a physiotherapist, while ballet dancers mainly turned to a physiotherapist and had better access to massage. The management survey showed substantial agreement with this pattern, and most of the ballet companies have a regular arrangement with a physiotherapist, often with on-site access. Ballet dancers were also twice as likely to be referred to a specialist. Other dancers were as likely to see a GP as a physiotherapist, which may well be a reflection of their financial situation. In Caroline Kitchin's survey of musical theatre dancers, 65% went to a physiotherapist, 39% to a GP and 22% to an osteopath.[6]

Treatment received

	Ballet professionals %	Contemporary professionals %	Other professionals %	Students %
Physiotherapy	78	52	39	55
Osteopathy	47	51	42	34
Massage	46	30	26	23
GP	9	16	39	23
Consultant	23	12	10	17
Acupuncture	14	21	16	4
Chiropractic	11	12	13	6
Counselling	negligible	3	3	3
Other	5	7	16	11

Treatment received (all dancers)

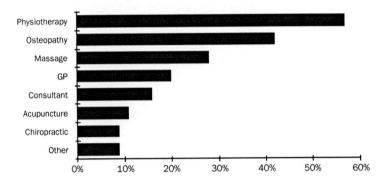

Paying for treatment

Most of the contemporary dancers had to pay for themselves, with very few being covered by insurance; one woman with a lower back injury had consulted six different practitioners at a total cost of £22,000, only

	Ballet professionals %	Contemporary professionals %	Other professionals %	Students %
Self	49	72	65	35
NHS	5	11	35	20
Insurance	32	6	negligible	20
Employer/ school	27	14	10	26

partly paid by insurance. Despite insurance cover, half of the ballet dancers had had to make at least some contribution. Students were more likely to have insurance or to rely upon the NHS. The companies' responses corroborated this picture; 46% of the companies had paid £100 or less in the previous year and only the ballet companies took out insurance. Again it can be seen that dancers in other styles had to rely substantially upon the NHS.

Paying for treatment

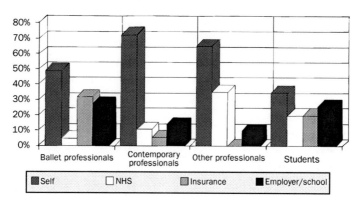

Additional costs of injury

The most common way in which companies coped with absence due to injury or illness was by rehearsing other dancers or understudies (36%), followed by reworking the choreography for fewer dancers (10%) or in the last resort taking on extra dancers (8%). Some companies reported a combination of these methods, depending upon the severity and duration of the injury. There are Equity/employer agreements providing for sick pay over an agreed number of weeks, but the smaller companies are often operating in a more informal manner and may experience great difficulties if one or more of the dancers has to be off for any period of time. In fact, only 58% of the injured professional dancers had taken days off work because of injury, compared to 83% of the injured students. The cost of coping with injury in the past year was reported as less than £1,000 by 61% of the companies, although one commercial management calculated that they had spent £38,000 taking on extra 'swings' (understudies) and paying for extra rehearsals to replace injured dancers.

Insecurity of the dancer's life

The reluctance to seek immediate professional help and the subsequent difficulty in affording treatment may in part be explained by seeing that less than half the companies offered 46 or more weeks of employment to dancers in the last financial year. The most common pattern was 37 weeks, with three companies offering only seasonal work to their dancers. Longer contracts were associated with greater likelihood of injury. However, the job insecurity inherent in working on short-term contracts may well inhibit dancers from seeking prompt treatment once they have been injured or taking rest to promote recovery. Independent dancers spoke of the pressure in a small company, with no covers and the extremely limited financial resources provided by project funding, to keep on working through an injury in order not to place the whole project in jeopardy.

Other questions

Prevalence of warming up

It is generally agreed that warming up appropriately before physical work is one way to reduce the risk of injury. For instance, Louis Galli found that Broadway dancers who took at least two classes a week and warmed up before every performance were injured 70% less often than those who did not.[12] The Healthier Dancer questionnaire therefore asked if the dancer warmed up.

The ballet dancers appeared to have more trouble than other dancers in warming up before rehearsal. This may be due to the difficulty of knowing when particular dancers are going to be needed, especially when new work is being choreographed.

In South Asian dance there is traditionally a long period of preparation of mind and body before performance, but no physical warm-up in the generally accepted Western sense. Now that some South Asian choreographers are stretching the tradition and demanding a new

Warming up

	Ballet professionals %	Contemporary professionals %	Other professionals %	Students %
Before class	87	88	73	91
Before rehearsal	77	93	90	78
Before performance	93	96	92	86

Warming up and cooling down

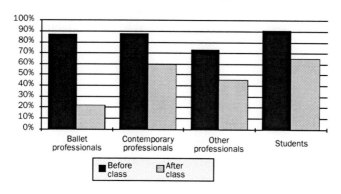

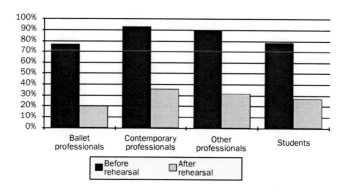

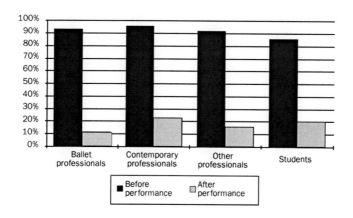

physicality of their dancers, there would seem to be a need to investigate appropriate warm-up methods for dancers using these traditional forms in a Western setting. Western warm-up methods might also have much to learn from the integration of mind and body fostered by the traditional Asian approach.

Prevalence of cooling down

Cooling down reduces the levels of excess hormones generated during vigorous activity and slowly lowers heart rate and body temperature. With appropriate stretches it can also help to prevent subsequent muscle soreness.

Cooling down

	Ballet professionals %	Contemporary professionals %	Other professionals %	Students %
After class	22	59	45	65
After rehearsal	20	36	31	27
After performance	11	23	16	20

In general, very few dancers said that they cool down. There seems to be widespread ignorance of the physical and physiological benefits of cooling down, similar to the situation in sports 15-20 years ago. Although those few dancers who **are** cooling down do so for an adequate amount of time, and more than half the contemporary dancers cool down after class, more education on this matter would seem to be necessary.

Smoking

Fully 36% of female dancers and 40% of male dancers admitted to smoking, with students being the worst offenders. The actual level is probably higher. Yet many of the health professionals consulted gave this as a major contributing factor to ill-health and injury, contributing to poor cardiovascular efficiency and therefore adversely affecting stamina and fatigue levels, as well as to the more widely recognised health risks.

Food and drink

Almost three-quarters of the dancers took some alcohol, but mostly within safe limits, 15% said they were on a diet and 61% were taking vitamins. One-third said they had obtained advice on nutrition from a magazine or TV programme, which are unlikely to be the most suitable sources of information on the particular high-energy requirements of a dancer. Students were more likely to have received some nutritional guidance from a teacher.

Psychological problems

The survey highlighted a large number of psychological problems, with some dancers ticking almost every category. More students reported depression, low self-confidence and eating problems, while contemporary professionals consistently reported more problems than

Psychological problems

	Ballet professionals %	Contemporary professionals %	Other professionals %	Students %
Over-use of alcohol/drugs	8	10	10	8
Difficulty in concentrating	13	16	12	24
Eating problems	19	15	10	26
External stress	35	63	61	48
Performance anxiety	36	38	49	29
General anxiety	54	66	51	57
Depression	45	45	43	54
Sudden drop in confidence	38	43	35	37
General low self-confidence	46	42	31	53
Tension with people	57	67	59	52

Some multiple replies were given

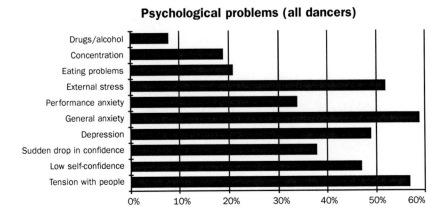

Psychological problems (all dancers)

ballet dancers, except in the areas of general self-confidence and eating problems. Asked to rank the problems in order of frequency, the managements reported a very similar perception of dancers' problems, but only 12% had any sort of regular arrangement with a counsellor.

Access to counselling
Several schools now have attached counselling facilities and encourage students to self-refer, although this is a relatively recent development. Of our sample, only 19% had used counselling as students and 22% as professionals. A quarter said that they had ready access to a counsellor at the moment, in contrast to the 44% who do not have such access but would like to.

Vocational training
Whereas only 18% of the ballet dancers felt that their training had not prepared them adequately for their life as a dancer, 43% of the contemporary dancers felt that it left a lot to be desired:

'I had fantastic dance education and training but absolutely no guidance as to what professional work consists of, where to go etc.'

'It was limited to purely technical training, with no vocational preparation, little academic input, poor choreographic input and quite a few myths and prejudices.'

'There are so many things to learn from experience but I would have valued information regarding: 1) performance effects on the nervous system 2) how to deal with the psychological trauma caused by the media 3) guilt in performance if a mistake is made 4) aspects of ageing/maturing as a dancer 5) how to teach 6) how to recognise and deal with injury.'

Background to research

With the many problems, especially psychological, highlighted by the surveys, the scene was set for the fitness and nutrition assessments.

References

1 Eva Ramel and Ulrich Moritz, 'Self-reported musculoskeletal pain and discomfort in professional ballet dancers in Sweden', *Scandinavian Journal of Rehabilitative Medicine* no. 26 (1994), pp. 11-16

2 *The Green List:* dance groups or individuals of professional status that are funded or have recently applied for funding from the Arts Council; *the White List:* dance companies and organisations who are regularly funded by the Arts Council. The Arts Council of England, London

3 Ann Bowling, 'Injuries to dancers: prevalence, treatment and perceptions of causes', *British Medical Journal* vol. 298 (1989) pp. 731-4

4 *Careers and Training in Dance and Drama,* (Institute of Manpower Studies, 1994)

5 The Council for Dance Education and Training, unofficial estimate, 1993.

6 Caroline Kitchin, 'Musical theatre: a dance injury survey', *Dancing Times* (March 1994), pp. 611-3

7 Editorial in *Dance Teacher* (January 1996)

8 Allan Ryan and Robert Stephens, 'The epidemiology of dance injuries' in *The Healthy Dancer*, same eds. (London, Dance Books, 1989)

9 Randolph Evans, Richard Evans, Scott Carvajal and Susan Perry 'A survey of injuries among Broadway performers', *American Journal of Public Health*, 86(10) (January 1996)

10 Tony Geeves, *The Safe Dance Project Report* (Australian Association for Dance Education (Ausdance), 1990)

11 *Injuries in sport and exercise* (Sports Council, 1993)

12 Louis Galli, 'Damage Control', *Dance Magazine* (December 1994)

Dancers: Yat Sen Chang/Lienz Chang: English National Ballet
Photograph: Anthony Crickmay

4

The fitness and nutritional research

THE FITNESS AND NUTRITIONAL RESEARCH

A risk business

Whatever the safeguards, dance is a risk business. Under extreme physical demands or in particularly challenging new movement, the frame of the dancer may give way at its weakest point. Nor will the psyche of the dancer sustain extreme stresses of performance indefinitely. Performance stress can also affect actors, politicians, teachers and many other professions. Dancers and sports people, however are unique. For them the whole body, physical and psychological, **is** the instrument. All-round fitness is a key to reducing the risk of injury, while repair of injury is only a last resort. Fitness is the best way to improve performance and ensure longer careers. This chapter examines the issue of physical fitness.

A dancer's problem

The medical and scientific communities are beginning to recognise that various forms of dance are as strenuous physically and as demanding as most sports activities. **Dancers are, in fact, among the supreme all-round athletes in our society.** It follows that professional dancers should be as well supported medically, physiologically and psychologically as other sportspeople. Although dancers are expected to perform continually for 15-20 years, all recent scientific and dance studies, including those conducted for this report, show that dancers face greater chances of suffering permanent disabilities than most other elite competitors. Why? Could it be that their training no longer provides the fitness levels which today's professional dance demands?

The rewards of fitness

Dancers must be fit enough to sustain the work they are required to do. With more power, they can jump higher. With more strength they can resist injury better. With more aerobic endurance, they can concentrate better throughout the day. With more anaerobic endurance they can sustain high-energy dance sequences better. With appropriate flexibility and strength they can more easily reach and hold the positions required. In other words, dancers and their teachers need to extend their understanding of fitness.

Fitness for dance

Physical fitness may be defined as 'the individual's ability to meet the demands of a specific physical task'. It is a composite which varies markedly, depending on an individual's age and level of performance. It incorporates aspects of endurance and stamina (aerobic fitness); speed and power (for the continued use of which anaerobic fitness applies); muscle strength; elements of body composition such as body fat and muscle mass; joint mobility; and body balance. Dance calls on all these fitness components to a very high degree. Regardless of performance level, sex and age, all dancers must seriously consider fitness if the artistic purpose is to be fulfilled.

The components of physical fitness

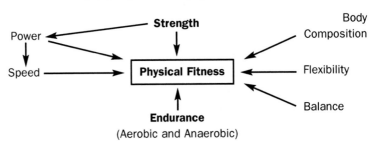

Data on the physiology of dance

Relatively little scientific data exist on aspects associated with the physiology of dance. Such data have been obtained from the study of rather a small number of dancers, with a limited range of variables, from research conducted in different parts of the world. It has, for example, been found that dancers show lower muscular strength, speed and endurance measured against other comparably active individuals,[1,2,3] with professional ballet dancers showing lower overall fitness than modern dancers.[4] Principally, however, we draw upon a pioneering and comprehensive study of British male and female dancers commissioned for this report from Dr Koutedakis, Dr Pacy and others.

British fitness deficiencies

Already at Dance UK's international conference **Training Tomorrow's Professional Dancers**, in September 1993, doubts were raised about inherited training methods and practices in professional dance.[5] Our research by Dr Koutedakis and Dr Pacy confirms these doubts. The main findings of this research were:

- British classical and contemporary dancers demonstrate approximately 5-7% less cardio-respiratory fitness than their US and Russian counterparts
- lack of fitness correlates with lower body injuries, by far the most common sites for male and female professional dancers
- female dancers have relatively less strength than men and have more lower body injuries
- when male ballet dancers were given a specific muscle-strengthening programme they suffered fewer lower body injuries
- many dancers have demonstrated a depressed immune system, which may well be caused by overwork, and increases susceptibility to such illnesses as colds and flu
- dancers' diets are wrongly balanced. They draw a high proportion of calories from fat and not enough from carbohydrates. They do not consume enough antioxidants (selenium, vitamins A, C and E), which again may well affect the immune system. Among the trace elements, only the iron intake from their diet meets current recommended levels.

Flexibility and fitness
For many years fitness has been equated in the dance world with flexibility or suppleness. Flexibility is just one component of fitness but is often the dancer's obsession. Flexibility is defined as 'the ability of the joint to move through a full range of movement'. Good flexibility usually indicates that the joint can move freely and that there are no serious anatomical or muscular limitations. Individuals will differ markedly in their natural flexibility and the degree to which it can be improved. Age, body type, gender and factors such as temperature, humidity, stress levels and whether or not the dancer regularly warms up may also influence the range of movement. Since there are no universally accepted flexibility test protocols, and those that do exist are extremely time-consuming, the researchers conducted no flexibility measurements for the present study.

Results of the fitness assessments

Body composition

Body weight may be divided into two components: body fat and lean body mass. In recent years, body fat assessments have replaced the simpler weight for height measures as a more accurate way of comparing the body composition of different active individuals. Muscle is denser than fat, so the relative proportion of lean body mass to body fat is reflected in body density;\ i.e. body density decreases as the proportion of body fat increases. However, very low levels of fat in females may lead to menstrual irregularities, which have recently been implicated in the incidence of osteoporosis (brittle-bone disease) in women athletes in their 30s, as well as in increased risks of stress fractures. The female dancers tested for this study had body fat values of around 20%, and the men 12%, which can be generally considered as acceptable for elite athletes. Not surprisingly, the ballet dancers were slightly leaner than the contemporary dancers.

Aerobic endurance and stamina, or aerobic fitness

Maximal Oxygen Uptake (VO_2max) values in mlO_2/kg/min obtained from dancers and untrained individuals				
Form of Dance	Country	Sex	Age	VO_2max
Contemporary	France	Males	22.0	64.6
Ballet	Russia	Males		63.0
Contemporary	USA	Males	24.6	61.8
Ballet	Russia	Females		58.0
Ballet	USA	Males	27.3	56.0
Contemporary*	UK	Males	26.6	55.7
Ballet*	UK	Males	25.8	53.2
Ballet	USA	Females	25.8	51.4
Students*	UK	Males	23.0	49.4
Students*	UK	Females	21.3	46.0
Untrained	UK	Males	25.0	44.0
Contemporary*	UK	Females	27.1	43.5
Ballet*	UK	Females	25.9	39.1
Untrained	UK	Females	25.0	36.0

* = Healthier Dancer Programme data

Our research shows that professional dancers and dance students in the UK have low aerobic endurance levels compared with their counterparts in other countries. Sometimes their levels are not much higher than those expected from untrained individuals. Physiological measurements obtained during the standard barre and centre practice sessions of daily class have shown that male and female dancers work at approximately 50% of their maximal aerobic endurance potential.[6] However, exercise intensity of at least 60% of the dancer's aerobic endurance potential is required to improve this important fitness component. In other words, the activity of dance alone is not enough to promote positive adaptations of the dancer's aerobic (i.e. endurance) system. Two or three

CASE HISTORY 4

Deborah Bull, principal dancer with the Royal Ballet; extracts from an article in *Dance UK News*, December 1995 (reprinted with permission)

'It wasn't until relatively recently that I discovered that the magical qualities 'energy' and 'stamina' were elements that could be worked on in the same way as pirouettes or entrechats... A couple of years ago I met a physiotherapist who checked my heart rate at the end of the Black Swan pas de deux and found it to be over 200 beats per minute. I was intrigued as to why he was so interested in it. How was this relevant to me and my work? It was the beginning of a long learning curve for me. For the first time in all my years as a dancer someone introduced the idea that perhaps dancers are not utilising the most efficient ways to achieve optimal performance, and that by improving fitness and nutrition I could achieve better results in performance and at the same time guard against injury.

'Consequently, my working practices have radically altered, with noticeable benefits. ... My increased fitness has meant that in performance I can focus on technique and artistry, and not on staving off total collapse. That in itself has made dancing a more satisfying experience. The knowledge that I have gained is a kind of support system, both physical and psychological. Knowing that I can contribute in such a positive way to my work acts for me as an antidote to pre-performance nerves. There is always luck involved when you go on the stage, but I feel that now I am not quite so dependent upon it.'

sessions a week, of at least 20 minutes, of some appropriate strenuous aerobic exercise such as swimming, cycling, skipping, circuits, aerobics or jogging, are necessary to achieve such adaptations.

Mean Peak Power (MPP), Mean Power (MP) and Time to Peak Power (TPP) values obtained from British elite athletes and dancers

Activity	Sex	MPP (Watts)	MP (Watts)	TPP (Seconds)
Rowers	Males	1140	880	5.1
Skiers	Males	982	685	5.4
Fencers	Males	809	673	6.6
Gymnasts	Males	790	690	6.0
Dancers (contemporary)*	Males	740	580	7.4
Rowers	Females	690	595	6.3
Dancers (ballet)*	Males	680	580	9.0
Dance students*	Males	650	510	7.1
Gymnasts	Females	580	500	7.0
Dance students*	Females	477	374	8.5
Dancers (contemporary)*	Females	465	359	8.3
Dancers (ballet)*	Females	410	329	8.5

* = Healthier Dancer Programme data

Speed, power and anaerobic fitness

Anaerobic fitness may be defined as 'the ability to continue to exercise at the highest possible work rate'. Biochemically, this is the ability for fast repeated muscular contractions (involving both speed and power) for short periods of time when the energy demand exceeds the ability of the aerobic system to supply it. This type of fitness is essential, therefore, to the execution of particularly demanding solos such as the dance of the Bluebird in *The Sleeping Beauty* in classical ballet, passages in *Troy Game* in contemporary dance, or the tap sequences in *Riverdance*.

Generally speaking, male contemporary dancers and young male ballet dancers showed satisfactory anaerobic fitness in our tests, but the female dancers performed less well compared to approximately equivalent elite athletes such as gymnasts or rowers. Genetic factors primarily influence the ability to sustain fast repetitive movements but appropriate preparation and training can produce greater power for a longer time. Anaerobic interval training and plyometrics (exercises which contain powerful rebounds) are the most popular methods for improving speed and power.

Mean Peak Torque values for the muscles involved in knee extension and knee flexion at 1.04 rad/sec, in British elite athletes and dancers

Activity	Sex	Knee Extension (Nm)	Knee Flexion (Nm)
Rugby players	Males	372	169
Rowers	Males	350	165
Skiers	Males	296	162
Fencers	Males	273	145
Squash players	Males	280	136
Rowers	Females	212	89
Dancers (contemporary)*	Males	196	94
Dance students*	Males	188	89
Dancers (ballet)*	Males	181	82
Squash players	Females	168	79
Dancers (contemporary)*	Females	133	68
Dance students*	Females	126	64
Dancers (ballet)*	Females	118	59

* = Healthier Dancer Programme data

Muscular strength

Muscular strength may be defined as 'the ability to overcome external resistance by muscular force'.

In our study dancers in general again showed lower muscle strength levels than other elite athletes. Research has shown that low strength levels are linked to decreased bone density,[3] which may increase susceptibility to stress fractures. Strength training, therefore, becomes essential over and above normal dance training. Most often this can be achieved through the use of weight and resistance training, by both male[7] and female dancers.[8] A note should be made here regarding the widely held belief that increased muscle strength inevitably means increased muscle size. This is not true if a correctly designed strength enhancement programme is adopted. For example, a subject whose strength increased by approximately 50% showed no increase in muscle size. Where dancers dislike using weights, other resistance exercises can be used such as body resistance methods and resistance-loaded equipment.

Importance of strength levels

Low back injuries are the most common form of injury in professional dancers, often due to an imbalance in the thigh muscles, that is, hamstrings to quadriceps. Our research also shows that the weaker the dancer is in the lower body, the more knee, ankle and foot injuries he or she has, and the more days away from dancing. An individually tailored programme for strengthening hamstrings resulted in a reduction in the rates of lower body injuries. We can thus see that it is important to do regular strength training as well as traditional dance classes. Female dancers were relatively weaker and demonstrated an even stronger relationship between lack of lower-body strength and reported injuries, so they would particularly benefit from strength training.

An encouraging experiment

The value of strength training in general can also be demonstrated through the results of a limited experiment by Dr Koutedakis and Dr Cross with male dancers of the Birmingham Royal Ballet.[7] This shows that, as with training for endurance and stamina, dance classes alone do not improve strength beyond certain levels. It follows that additions to training are necessary to prepare dancers for current performance demands.

The immune system

As an adjunct to the main fitness assessment, our researchers took saliva samples from some of the dancers in order to test the levels of the protective compounds immunoglobulin A and lysozyme, the resting levels of which are regarded as good markers indicating the optimal function of the immune system. They found that the resting levels of these two compounds were considerably lower in the dancers than in non-dancers, or in elite rowers and swimmers. This may well relate to a susceptibility to infection of the upper respiratory tract; indeed, three of the dancers reported chest pain and coughing for at least five weeks. Increased volumes of work, frequent performances, inappropriate eating patterns and low environmental temperature have all been suggested as factors which would depress the blood concentrations, but further research needs to be done on this topic before categorical statements can be made.

Results of the nutritional assessments

Dancers' diets

Some of the dancers participating in the fitness assessments agreed to keep food diaries for four to five days. When the researchers analysed these food diaries in detail, they found that the energy consumed ranged from 3,000 down to 1,300 kcal per day, with the average being 2,650 for male dancers and 1,980 for females. These values were close to those obtained previously for competition gymnasts and are slightly less than the averages of about 2,800 and 2,100 for untrained males and females of the same age range and approximate body weight in the general population.

Balance between fats and carbohydrates

The dancers obtained only about 50% of their energy from carbo-hydrates. It is generally agreed that for healthy eating, carbohydrates should supply closer to 60% of daily calories. In addition, dancers exercising intensively may need more carbohydrate than normal in order to maintain their glycogen stores. Refined carbohydrates, such as are available from highly processed and 'junk' foods, outnumbered the complex carbohydrates which come from such foods such as bread, rice, potatoes, pasta and cereals. With wholemeal bread and brown rice there would also be the added advantage of a high fibre content. The dancers consumed more fatty foods than other sportspeople, with percentages higher than the generally accepted UK goal of 30%.

Low vitamin levels linked to injury

It is also worth noting that vitamin C levels in the dancers were substantially lower than for rowers, cyclists or gymnasts. This perhaps reflects a reduced intake of fresh fruit and vegetables, but in any case means that they have fewer antioxidants available. Those dancers with inadequate levels of vitamin C, vitamin D and vitamin E demonstrated significantly higher rates of musculoskeletal injury compared to their counterparts with adequate levels. The low levels of antioxidants can be linked in turn to the functioning of the immune system. Although the causes are not known for certain, it has been suggested that overtraining - prolonged and intensive exercise levels - as well as sudden increases in the level of physical activity, lack of sufficient physical rest to recover properly and insufficient nutrition may contribute to this malfunction of the immune system.

Incidence of vegetarianism

Around 30-40% of the dancers tested were vegetarians, which is a very high proportion compared to the general population. It is evident, however, that vegetarianism is on the increase, particularly among young people. A meatless diet can certainly help to increase the proportion of energy obtained from carbohydrates; most meats and meat products are high in fats, so a loss of these will require the energy supply to be made up from carbohydrate. Being vegetarian does, however, require a more detailed knowledge of nutrition than eating the standard Western diet, in order to ensure a proper supply of nutrients. This is especially important for dancers trying to control their weight. The researchers were surprised to discover that none of the dancers had received professional nutritional advice, a finding which was also borne out in the individual questionnaires.

Fluid intake

Since one of the messages from the Healthier Dancer Conference in 1990 was the loss of performance and increased risk of injury if fluid is not replaced while exercising, it was encouraging to find that nearly all the dancers on test knew about the importance of drinking regularly throughout the day.

Resting Energy Expenditure

Daily energy expenditure consists of the resting energy expenditure (REE), which is required to maintain the normal body processes, plus the energy required for physical work during the day. In general, non-athletic people have an REE of approximately 70% of the total daily energy expenditure. The contemporary dancers tested here had the same REE as the normal population, whereas the female ballet dancers were slightly under, at around 1,110 kcal a day. However, some previous studies have reported ballet dancers as having very low REEs of around 900 kcal, which suggests that those dancers were gradually starving themselves.

Messages for the profession

From the experience of testing dancers for the purposes of this inquiry, it would appear that at least some of the messages regarding healthy eating and drinking for the maximal performance desired by all dancers, their teachers and managements are beginning to be absorbed. Nevertheless, there is still much work to be done, not only as regards good practice in nutrition and fluid intake, but also in improving levels of strength and endurance in dancers.

References

1 D T Kirkendall and L H Calabrese, 'Physiological aspects of dance', *Clinics in Sports Medicine*, 2(1983), pp. 525-37

2 Yiannis Koutedakis and Craig Sharp, 'Fitness assessment of elite competitors', *Rheumatology Now*, 1(1990), pp. 18-20

3 Roger Wolman, Peter Clark, Eugene McNally, Mark Harries and Jonathan Reeve, 'Menstrual state and exercise as determinants of spinal trabecular bone density in female athletes', *British Medical Journal*, 301(1990), pp. 516-18

4 Robin Chmelar, Barry Schultz, Robert Ruhling, Terry Shepherd, Michael Zupan and Sally Sevey Fitt, 'A physiologic profile comparing levels and styles of female dancers', *Physician & Sportsmedicine*, 16(7)(1988), pp. 87-96

5 *Tomorrow's Dancers*, Laban Centre for Movement and Dance (London, 1994)

6 J L Cohen, K R Segal, I Witriol and W D McArdle, 'Cardio-respiratory responses to ballet exercise and the maximal oxygen intake of elite ballet dancers', *Medicine & Science in Sports & Exercise*, 14(1982), pp. 212-17

7 Yiannis Koutedakis, Victor Cross and Craig Sharp 'The effects of strength training in male ballet dancers', *Impulse* (in press, 1996)

8 Margaret Stalder, Bruce Noble and John Wilkinson 'The effects of supplemental weight training for ballet dancers', *Journal of Applied Sport Science Research*, 4(3)(1990), pp. 95-102

Dancer: Roman Rykin: English National Ballet
Photograph: Anthony Crickmay

5

The psychological research

THE PSYCHOLOGICAL RESEARCH

Aims of the research

The aim of the psychological research was to substantiate and deepen the picture provided by the Healthier Dancer questionnaire regarding the psychological and emotional lives of professional dancers in Great Britain today. Furthermore, we wanted to see how dancers' emotional needs might be directly addressed through psychological preparation and education, counselling and therapy methods.

Need to take an integrated approach

Part of the perennial problem in providing adequate support for dancers' psychological and emotional health needs is the history of stigmatisation of anything psychological. One aspect of this situation is the fear that psychological investigation destroys creative capacity by removing the neurosis which 'fuels' it. However, it is important to bear in mind that dancers, like the rest of the population, do not neatly divide into a Cartesian mind-body split, or in other words, into psychological 'versus' physical, especially when one is looking at injury problems.

Underlying questions

Hence, when we are considering the so-called psychological and emotional aspects of dancers' lives and what kind of problems may develop in them, we are in a way asking: 'Which aspects of dancers' health, wellbeing and injury can be usefully understood and addressed from a psychological, as well as a physical, point of view?' We are also asking: 'To what extent is there an awareness of psychology amongst today's dancers which usefully equips them with a sense of personal responsibility and insight into the deeper and internal sources of some of their difficulties as dancers?'

Interviews with dancers

Selection of interviewees

The investigation mainly took the form of interviews with dancers and with counsellors working with dancers. Initially, dancers were chosen from those who had volunteered for interviews at the time of completing the health and injury questionnaire. After the first round, other dancers were asked to participate in order to balance the survey.

Methodology

For the dancers, an extensive interview schedule was devised which addressed the following main areas:

- personal and educational background
- work-related problems
- the dancers' awareness of lifestyle, self-care and stress management issues
- the larger professional issues bearing on these problems.

Each interview took the dancer through the schedule and lasted between one and two hours.

Age, sex, style

Thirty-eight dancers were interviewed altogether, 26 female and 12 male. Overall, 25 of the dancers were professional and 13 were third-year dance students in two different contemporary performance groups. Of the total group, 10 were ballet dancers, 20 were contemporary dancers (18 in companies and 2 independents); 8 were South Asian dancers. Ages ranged from 19 to 37, with an average age for the females of 25 years and for the males of 27 years.

Support systems

Most of the dancers came from families who had maintained a positive and supportive attitude towards their child's choice of dance as a career (32 out of the 38). About half of the dancers currently had stable partners, all but one of them supportive; indeed 11 of the 18 partners were dancers themselves. In 33 cases the dancer felt that they had at least one person in their life in whom they could confide and 27 lived with other people, i.e. with a partner, friends or family, so they were in the main not leading a solitary life.

Dance and educational background

There were some noteworthy differences between dance styles regarding the age at which dancers started training and the length of time spent with one particular teacher. Sixteen of the 20 contemporary or independent dancers did not start their dance training until the age of 16 years or more, compared with only 2 of the 10 ballet dancers, both of whom were, not surprisingly, male, whereas the female ballet dancers had all started dancing in childhood.

Length of time spent with one particular teacher

The South Asian dancers had by far the longest relationships with their 'gurus' (spiritual masters as well as physical teachers) and from an earlier age. Two of them had worked with their own guru for 17 years or more, that is, starting from early childhood. In comparison, the longest teacher-student relationships within other dance styles were reported by two ballet dancers and one contemporary dancer who had developed good long-term relationships with dance teachers as coaches later on in their professional lives, of between six and nine years. Western dance students usually have many different teachers, who change from year to year, especially in the senior vocational schools. This means that dancers can have difficulties developing a relationship with their teachers. It is generally felt, however, that students need to have different teachers in order to develop. Once ballet dancers have joined a company, they start to have a more solid relationship with the company teachers. In addition, it has to be remembered that dancers move around from company to company nowadays more than in the past, so it is useful to be able to cope with different teachers.

Effects of teaching

Two-thirds of the contemporary dancers felt that, on balance, their teaching had been positive. The South Asian dancers were evenly divided on this question, but placed a more positive interpretation upon their teachers being critical, perhaps because the length of the association had given the dancer the opportunity to work through the dancer-teacher relationship. They perceived the teacher's comments as being of overall value. By contrast, two-thirds of the ballet dancers felt that their teachers' criticisms had affected them negatively. They gave many more instances than the other dancers of 'damaging' comments made by their teachers, who were accused of being unconstructively critical and giving no help with the individual needs of the dancer's body. They wanted their teachers to be tough but fair.

Possible reasons for the differences between the styles

We may wonder if there is a marked difference between the way that South Asian and ballet teachers give criticism, or whether ballet dancers are less able to make use of criticism. Dance teachers could perhaps think more about how to be constructively critical and must be on their guard against criticising out of resentment or envy of the dancer's youth and future career. Again, perhaps this is more likely in Western dance, where the dancers' life is so much shorter; in South Asian dance the performer is generally considered not to reach his or her peak until the age of 40-50.

Danger of outmoded attitudes

There seems to be still established in many dance teachers' minds an underlying assumption that negative criticism is the best way to bring out the best performance from their students. This attitude, once pervasive, is nowadays perceived as outdated in most walks of life. Carl Rogers has stressed the importance in a learning environment of establishing empathy, warmth and what he calls 'unconditional positive regard'.[1] Excessive external discipline does not encourage personal responsibility and works against the development of self-esteem. The student needs the chance to internalise the discipline initially imposed by the teaching. This is generally agreed to be a challenging aspect of human development in any sphere; it is one to which the dance world in particular should pay more attention.

Preparation for transition

Bearing out the responses in the main Healthier Dancer Programme questionnaires, the interviewed dancers mostly had some idea of what they were planning to do when they had to stop dancing. One-third saw themselves becoming teachers, while taking a course of study was another popular option. Many of the ideas given showed that the dancers would like to stay in the arts professions or related fields. Perhaps unsurprisingly, the third-year students seemed to have given very little thought to this issue.

Causes of injury

Ballet dancers showed the highest awareness of a link between injury and psychological or emotional events, coming up with five different instances each on average, whereas the 18 contemporary dancers managed only 15 comments between them. Across all dance styles the most frequently mentioned psychological precipitants of injury were depression, performance-related stress and decreased self-esteem, which correspond with the findings of the main survey. Important for the ballet dancers was managerial pressure to dance, which will be discussed later.

Effects of injury

The most common psychological effects of injury were reported as being depression, decreased self-esteem and general anxiety. Some, however, had also found being injured a positive experience on balance, reporting such sentiments as 'I felt I could live my life for the first time', 'I learned to care for myself', 'I actually felt happier and able to relax'.

Stage fright

Almost a quarter of the dancers reported experiencing panic attacks on stage, blanking out in performance, being unable to move. For many, this was the first time they had talked about stage fright with anyone and they did not understand why it had happened. One dancer reported feeling as if she was 'wading through glue' during a major debut. This may imply a lack of neuro-muscular control which could be physically dangerous. Anecdotal evidence from other branches of the performing arts suggests that many other performers suffer from stage fright but are ashamed to discuss it with even their closest colleagues. Almost all the dancers who had suffered severe stage fright had failed to seek help in understanding it and trying to prevent further instances.

Professional issues for ballet dancers

Ballet dancers complained of a lack of professional feedback in their working lives. Often they suffered from anxiety, depression or a sudden drop in self-esteem when they were not cast in a particular role, with no reason given. A new artistic director could ask a dancer who had been with the company for many years to leave because in his opinion the dancer no longer 'looked right' or was dancing poorly. Sometimes this kind of announcement of redundancy had been made extremely insensitively. For instance, one dancer had been told the news by a member of the ballet staff at the stage door after a performance. The dancers felt unable to approach the management to find out the thinking behind these decisions or to discuss how their personal career might develop within the company. This meant that they felt frustrated and often angry with the management, but powerless to change anything. In a very competitive situation, there was the tacit threat for the female dancers of 'there are plenty more where you came from', even if this was not actually enunciated. Personal assertiveness became easier only with promotion up the ladder, when the dancers felt in a safer position to speak up.

Professional issues for independents

Independent dancers felt particularly depressed at the end of a project. With no work in immediate prospect, they lost their sense of themselves as a professional dancer and became concerned about financial insecurity. During a project they had to put in long hours and be completely dedicated, almost to the exclusion of any other life, thus quickly becoming exhausted. Not knowing when the next job might come up or when the next grant might be awarded created difficulties in pacing, in both the short- and medium-term. 'It's all or nothing.' As soon as they entered the profession they had to be prepared to freelance, in effect to run themselves as a business. For this they needed skills of self-presentation, auditioning, CV writing and time management that were not covered in much detail during training. Some of the schools had offered sessions on these topics to students in the last year before graduating, but the dancers felt they needed time to absorb these matters and would have preferred them as a regular part of the core curriculum in the last year, rather than as one-off events.

Self-help strategies

Again, the approach to self-help seemed to divide along the lines of the dance style. Ballet dancers recognised the build-up of tension and then tended to respond to it, for instance by taking a hot bath, watching TV or having a big meal at the end of the day. They used massage as a post-stress technique and mentioned more remedial treatments than preventative ones. The contemporary and South Asian dancers, on the other hand, used a number of strategies such as yoga, meditation, t'ai chi, Alexander Technique and release techniques and seemed more

---

CASE HISTORY 5

'A' was a promising *corps de ballet* dancer who had a back injury which needed major surgery. She was back performing on stage in just over six months but probably came back too quickly through being anxious not to be left behind. She developed another injury, so had to rest and just do walk-on parts. Then she slipped down some steps and dislocated her kneecap. This meant a minor operation and another six months' break. After this her dancing was constantly plagued by minor injuries. These repeated setbacks left her feeling anxious, disillusioned, frustrated and constantly worried about the threat of re-injuring. She found it hard to concentrate and absorb what was being taught. Her confidence dropped dramatically and she found it hard to cope generally.

She was referred to a dance psychologist. Her primary problem was a high level of anxiety due to the number and severity of the injuries she had sustained and to the long periods away from the dancing environment. She learnt techniques to help concentration and control nerves, to relax and to help learning. Time management and assertiveness training gave her confidence and control over other aspects of her life that were affecting her dancing. Throughout this process she constantly had goals to work for, both short- and long-term. This was important to help motivation.

'A' made it back into the company, was promoted and then made a conscious decision to stop dancing and pursue a different career. She is now studying psychology at university.

'Overall, the help and constant support I received were invaluable. I have been able to develop to become a more focused and productive dancer and person.'

attuned to the idea of prevention and positive health. Interestingly enough, however, it was two of the ballet dancers who used visualisation, which may reflect the success of the new occupational psychology support system in their company.

Major professional issues relating to emotional problems

Responses here contrasted the life of a dancer in a large company with that of the solo dancer or one working in a small supportive group. Company dancers felt that they received too much group training. Being part of a group is important, but people have very different experiences of groups and some might benefit from more individual work. This was usually only available in the top ranks of the company, where the leading artists were individually coached. Furthermore, working long hours six days a week did not leave enough time for rest and the dancers felt they were permanently on the go. In a big institution it was hard for the dancers to discover their true identity; they felt that the structure encouraged emotional immaturity and infantilism. Younger dancers in particular were left to fend for themselves. Having services available such as physiotherapy and counselling was not enough if the dancers did not feel confident about using them or, worse still, were afraid of being stigmatised as 'unreliable' if they did. Dancers needed to be encouraged to use the services appropriately.

Injury-related problems in companies

There were particular problems related to the management of injury. As well as having to cope with the problems experienced by any injured dancer, as discussed previously, the company dancers perceived a huge pressure on them to perform while injured. It is true that this pressure may be as much in the dancer, reluctant to lose the chance of a good role or status in the company, as from the management, but the dancers perceived it as coming from the management. They deeply resented this culture of insecurity and felt that the staff exploited the dancers' fear of what would happen if they refused to go on. A vicious circle thus developed, in which the staff might not be aware of the full extent of the injury or might not even have asked, while the dancer was afraid to be too explicit or assertive.

Issues of redundancy

In the independent sector, interviewed dancers felt that audiences and promoters failed to value the older dancers' experience. New dancers were arriving all the time from the various dance courses. Preference was given to the fresh and new, while years of hard work brought few rewards. These dancers felt unsupported by most of the existing structures in dance, when theoretically they should have been at the peak of their physical and emotional capacity. If they had not worked in a major company they were unable to turn to the Dance Companies' Resettlement Fund although many would have welcomed careers advice. (These interviews took place before the launch of the Dancers' Trust, which now supports the non-company dancer with career advice and retraining.)

Use of counselling

Around one-third of the dancers interviewed had used counselling at some time or another, a slightly higher proportion than in the main survey. By far the most common reason for seeking help was the need to manage injury, although a large variety of reasons were given. They were universal in their view that the counsellor had to have some background in dance to be of real use and to understand the pressures of this way of life. One suggestion was that counselling techniques should be taught to those students and dancers who were interested. This would not only give them a greater insight into their own emotional life but would help to develop skills which might stand them in good stead in later life even if they did not become professional counsellors themselves.

Interviews with counsellors

Finding the counsellors

Information was gathered from interviews with twelve counsellors or individuals working with dancers in a closely related capacity. These twelve, eight women and four men, were located by asking around the dance networks, advertising in dance journals and liaising with the British Association for Performing Arts Medicine. More had been expected, but none have subsequently come forward, so it may be that other health professionals, such as GPs and physiotherapists, are taking the brunt of the counselling role which is often called for in the treatment of injury. (Indeed, another research project found that dancers felt that interpersonal and counselling skills were more important than clinical skills for a successful physiotherapist.[3])

Different working situations

Of the twelve, four counsellors were formally attached to dance schools, two to companies or other dance institutions; six were working from a general private counselling or psychotherapy practice. One of the company counsellors was offering his services free of charge, while the other was officially employed by the company.

Different approaches

Most counsellors used primarily the explorative approaches of psychodynamic and humanistic psychology with their dance clients. Only three used cognitive-behavioural approaches to help dancers in a more focused way with specific performance-related issues. Two counsellors used drama and art therapy; one used movement and bodywork.

Different trainings and performing arts experience

The counsellors themselves had a variety of professional trainings and some also had other professional functions in the dance institution where they worked, such as dance teacher, administrator or occupational psychologist. One was specifically trained as a HIV/AIDS counsellor. Five of the counsellors had been professional dancers and one a professional opera singer. Of the remainder, three had substantial amateur experience in dance or music, while three had personal experience in the performing arts. As could be anticipated, counsellors' views on the value of a personal performing arts background related to their own situation, as did their views on the usefulness of watching the dancer/client in class or another work situation.

Modes of payment

Sessions in institutions were usually free to the dancer, whereas the dancer had to pay for counselling with a private practitioner. In these cases, it was not unusual for the counsellor to subsidise, sometimes heavily, the cost of the dancer's treatment, sometimes compromising his or her own earnings, out of sympathy for the dancer's plight and lack of financial resources.

Settings

Most of the counsellors saw dancers on an individual basis; two saw groups of dancers, usually students. Dancers were seen for anything between one and ten sessions. This tended to involve some crisis work, consultation and referral on where necessary. Ten of the counsellors took on a small proportion of dancers as long-term clients, i.e. for 2-3 years, usually with weekly sessions. For those counsellors working in institutions, it is perhaps worth pointing out that this means that a significant proportion of the counsellors' usually very limited time is unavailable for more general use with dancers. This problem could be reduced either by developing counselling facilities elsewhere for the dancer with longer-term needs or by increasing the time available for counsellors within these institutions.

Links with other professionals

More practically, there is a very real issue of privacy. If dancers' counselling is to be kept confidential, the question arises of the degree of visibility of the counsellor within the institution and the best way for the counsellor to interact with the other professionals involved in the dancers' artistic and personal needs. The counsellors in this study varied widely in their views on these questions. While seven of the counsellors described their setting as 'multidisciplinary', this varied from traditional medical multidisciplinary teams attached to a private practice to alternative medicine teams attached to a body conditioning studio and to therapists attached to a private psychotherapy clinic. Some counsellors worked closely with the physiotherapists involved with the dancer, others with the relevant dance teacher, GP or nutritionist. The best network for maximising dancers' emotional and physical health seems yet to be discovered. Two comments from the counsellors' interviews are offered for thought:

'To work effectively with an individual dancer, the counsellor must have a solid working familiarity with the dance company dynamics and politics.'

'The teacher-physiotherapist-counsellor triumvirate is essential for the dancers' artistic and emotional development and welfare during training. There must be good communication between these three figures.'

Types of dancers seen

Most counsellors saw both student and professional dancers, in varying proportions which changed over time. One specialised in dealing with retiring professionals, while another saw retiring and retired dancers for long-term consultation in her private clinic. Three counsellors saw other staff members as well as dancers. Although there is only a small provision of counselling, ballet and contemporary styles are more or less equally catered for. Interestingly enough, however, the only two professional dance companies in this study making use of a counsellor officially are both large ballet companies, whereas three out of the four dance schools using counsellors specialise in contemporary dance.

Particular qualities of dancers

When asked whether dancers manifested any particular qualities as clients for counselling, half of the counsellors felt they were no different from the bulk of the general population. Others found a high degree of compliance on the one hand, and qualities of hard work and commitment on the other, which seemed to be transferred by the dancers from their dancing to their capacity to use counselling effectively.

Types of problems presented

The most common problems for which dancers sought help were the emotional effects of injury, problems surrounding the dancers' identity as dancers, problems of work or private relationships. Only five counsellors had had reason to discuss HIV/AIDS. The underlying causes, as perceived by the counsellors, were most frequently cited as a problematic teacher-dancer relationship, damaging teaching styles, the emotional immaturity of dancers and eating difficulties.

Suggestions for improvement

Counsellors were asked what kinds of intervention, both preventative measures and/or educational input, might help to improve dancers' psychological and emotional health. They came up with a variety of suggestions, the most common being to find ways of encouraging personal responsibility in dancers and to develop health education as part of the dancer's vocational training and professional development.

References
1 Carl Rogers *Client Centred Therapy* (London, Constable, 1951/1995)
2 Carl Rogers *On Becoming a Person* (London, Constable, 1961/1995)
3 Britt Tajet-Foxell (unpublished thesis)

Dancers: David Toole/Helen Baggett: CanDoCo Dance Company
Photograph: Anthony Crickmay

6

Findings from the worlds of sports and medicine

FINDINGS FROM THE WORLDS OF SPORTS AND MEDICINE

'We have to do all that an athlete has to do - and then we have to smile!'

Another element in the Healthier Dancer research was the collation of information and advice from experts in dance medicine, sports medicine and sports science. The sports world has investigated many problems similar to those in dance and come up with some solutions which could equally well be applied to dance, given the will and resources.

Getting the right treatment for injury

Different types of injuries
Both dance and sports injuries may be **acute** i.e. of sudden onset, as in traumatic events such as a sprained ankle or a torn muscle; or they may be **chronic** i.e. of slow or insidious onset, as in the category of 'overuse' injuries and as in many acute injuries which partly heal, but settle into a much longer-term lower-grade disturbance.

The importance of immediate treatment
For all except truly minor injuries, the most important factor is that the injured person is seen as soon as possible, preferably immediately. With any injury, immediate First Aid, treatment and rest may prevent months of pain and discomfort. A few days' rest may prevent the development of a chronic injury, resulting in several weeks' enforced lay-off. Chronic injuries can last a long time – even, at worst, the rest of a dancer's career – if not treated properly. Some authorities have estimated that 80% of ballet dancers' injuries are chronic and in the Bowling survey two-thirds of the dancers were carrying an injury which interfered with their dancing.[1]

Necessary conditions for successful treatment
Lack of immediate access to specialist treatment via the NHS, or the inability to pay, means that the injury is too often left until it has become really disabling, by which time it will probably take many more sessions to clear than if immediate treatment had been sought and available. In order for immediate access to be possible, the patient must receive support and co-operation from his or her GP. Either patient or

GP must know which dedicated professional should next look at the injury if it is not completely straightforward. Payment must not be a barrier. Finally, proper rehabilitation programmes must be drawn up with the full involvement of the patient and the coach, trainer or teacher, as appropriate.

Need to recognise limits of experience

There are benefits for all health professionals in recognising the value of other approaches if their own treatment is failing to produce the expected results. 'An expert is someone who knows when to call in an expert.' We were told of one patient who came to an orthopaedic specialist in rehabilitative techniques after 18 months of osteopathic treatment had failed to clear up a back problem; the general opinion is that a patient should be referred if 5-6 such sessions fail to produce progress.

The importance of specialist treatment

Just as important is the need for specialised diagnosis. It is absolutely essential to reach the correct conclusion before commencing treatment. Whereas the ordinary person can usually still manage to earn their living while carrying an injury, the professional has to recover fully from injury in order to be able to work. Injuries to dance professionals must be seen as an **occupational** hazard, which means that specialised knowledge is required for both treatment and rehabilitation. Every activity has its own particular injury patterns and a practitioner able to treat long-distance runners, for example, is not necessarily as effective in dealing with the problems of a tennis player. In the same way, some injuries are specific to dance and are therefore hard for a non-specialist to diagnose accurately.

Procedure in the absence of specialist advice

If a practitioner with this detailed activity-specific knowledge is not available, however, someone with experience of treating injuries in other sports will at least have an understanding of the possible musculoskeletal problems and know how to examine the person properly. He or she will recognise the pressures upon the patient, such as fear of missing out on training, fear of losing competitive edge, fear of not being able to recover to the level sustained before the injury, worry about how to pay for the necessary treatment and whether the injury will adversely affect future performance and even income. The practitioner will recognise the pressures of intense competition, which mean that extra firmness is needed to say 'no, you cannot return to full workload yet'.

Application to performing arts medicine

The practitioner experienced in treating sports injuries should have some idea of the similar pressures upon the performing artist, although the types of injury presented by a musician, for example, may be just as different from those of a dancer as a runner's are from those of a tennis player. Musicians' injuries occur mainly in the upper body or limbs and often affect the joints, whereas dancers predominantly suffer soft tissue injuries in the lower body. However, many of the musicians' injuries are similarly categorised as 'overuse'. Dedicated physicians have established a few NHS performing-arts clinics which cater mainly to the needs of musicians, but most of these are in London and depend upon the goodwill of a handful of doctors.

Importance of rehabilitation programmes

Once the programme of treatment has begun, thought has to be given to the process of full recovery, or rehabilitation. It is now known that physical fitness deteriorates very quickly if the patient is immobile; even heart patients are now encouraged to move around gingerly just a couple of days after surgery. Elite athletes in the peak of fitness can recover very quickly from most injuries and have a very high degree of motivation, so they need different rehabilitation techniques from the recreational athlete, although the treatment is very much the same. Sports physicians advise that injured players should always be kept as part of the team, which helps them to cope psychologically and therefore to recover more quickly. Each injured athlete should have an individual rehabilitation plan. In this way, he or she can see the steps along the way to a full return to work. If something then goes wrong, the plan can be re-tailored. This is something that really requires expert knowledge. Especially with top performers, there must be enough time to rest and to allow the body to repair itself in its own time; healing cannot be rushed. Apart from the positive benefits to the people involved, the development of appropriate rehabilitation programmes in sport has influenced ideas of more general application, for instance on the role and importance of exercise as a treatment in itself.

Importance of multi-disciplinary approach

Before the patient returns to full activity, it is most important to identify the underlying cause of the injury. Especially with overuse and chronic injuries, both practitioner and patient should understand the pattern of the physical activity required and assess its physiological requirements. It may be that changes in technique are required. Some clinics have adopted a multi-disciplinary approach, whereby diagnosis of an injury involves not only the physician, but also a physiotherapist and a teacher or coach familiar with the patient's area of activity. In this way the patient can be helped to improve those elements of poor technique which may be causing the problem. Biomechanical assessments may be extremely important for establishing the root cause of recurrent injuries.

Incorporation of psychology into a multi-disciplinary approach

Studies in sports have found that athletes who have experienced a major life event, such as bereavement, divorce or even moving home, are significantly more likely to be injured and to have a severe injury. It also appears that both athletes and dancers have high pain thresholds, probably developed in training, which may affect the rate of recovery and have important implications for the risk of re-injury. Obviously, the athlete needs to be psychologically fit as well as physically fit, since injury can cause fear, doubt, loss of confidence, vulnerability and decline in skill. Injured athletes have been shown to cope better if they are taught to understand and manage their emotional response at the various stages of the recovery process. For this a practised and sympathetic psychologist is required, as well as support from family and friends. Otherwise the patient may be treated with initial success, but is likely to re-injure after returning to the activity.[2] Herein lies a particularly strong case for the multi-disciplinary approach, supporting the sportsperson or performing artist with specialised facilities.

Paying for treatment

Storing up problems for the future

As mentioned previously, at the moment a large number of patients are not able to get treatment quickly after an injury without having to pay. Even those who are covered by medical insurance usually need a GP referral before beginning treatment. There are delays in obtaining appointments with GPs and some reluctance on the GPs' part to refer patients to specialists. The Sports Council survey found that 44% of athletes rated their GPs' advice as poor and complained of doctors' unsympathetic attitudes to sporting injuries.[3] Recent moves towards fundholding GPs, and hospitals setting up as independent trusts, have made it much more difficult for even sympathetic doctors to obtain speedy effective treatment for sportspeople under the NHS. This means that injury clinics are now seeing a lot of patients with problems compounded by inadequate first treatment. These injuries may well become chronic.

Paying for private treatment: subsidy from practitioner

As injured dancers and sportspeople increasingly turn to private practitioners, another significant problem is the inability to pay full rates. Private practitioners in these fields admit that they often subsidise treatment, either by charging lower rates or by agreeing to spread payments over a period of time. Several experienced practitioners would be happy to see more dancers but simply could not carry the cost.

Limitations of insurance policies

Most currently-available insurance schemes focus on covering the costs of surgery and hospital in-patient care, placing less emphasis on such out-patient treatments as physiotherapy, osteopathy and podiatry (which are often the ones that dancers and sportspeople wish to consult first). Even those schemes which do make some provision for this type of cover will almost certainly not pay for counselling sessions or nutrition advice, however desirable. Yet it is generally agreed that only 2% of dance injuries require surgery. There would thus seem to be a need for a scheme which primarily gave access to out-patient treatment, with the back-up of tests and surgery only when required. This could help both company and independent dancers.

Pilot study required on companies

If such an insurance policy could be found, it would be interesting to compare the costs and management implications for a company relying on insurance for these out-patient treatments with another company reimbursing direct treatment costs up to a certain amount. Interestingly enough, when Boston Ballet decided to pay directly for a range of treatments such as physiotherapy and chiropractic, it found that more than half of the injuries cost less than $500 to treat. It hopes that the much lower claim rate will substantially reduce its insurance premiums.[4]

Models of insurance schemes for individuals

Fitness instructors and dance teachers with recognised qualifications can take out individual private medical insurance at group rates through membership of their professional bodies. A similar arrangement is now available for Equity members. All these schemes, however, are optional, what the insurers term 'self-selecting', so the rates are still relatively high. In sport there are some arrangements whereby all the people in a certain category are covered, which brings the cost down still further. The British Olympic Association, for instance, allocates a set number of places for each governing body in a group insurance scheme which covers all hospital costs and some out-patient treatments without needing individual proposal forms. The International Athletics Federation scheme covers some Class A squad athletes and partly reimburses treatment costs. Some governing bodies of the more hazardous sports such as rugby and judo have included an element of medical insurance in their Association membership, but this does not cover ordinary sports injuries. In Australia part of every sports club membership, even at the lowest age, is taken to cover the costs of private medical insurance. With many more people in the scheme, the risk is spread and so the premiums can be kept low. A similar industry-wide scheme for dancers, perhaps in conjunction with other performers, would enable the individual dancer to benefit from the same cover as the dancers in the major companies, and would repay further investigation.

A look at prevention issues and strategies

The fundamental importance of prevention and education

Time and time again, health professionals have stressed their conviction that prevention is better than cure. No-one is happy to provide only 'Band-Aid' treatment; rather everyone wants to keep people fit and well. Sometimes this means arguments with players and coaches, dancers and teachers. All too often dancers and sportspeople are not very interested in health and injury until they run into a problem themselves. However, the body is not a machine which can be replaced if it breaks down. Once used and worn down, it cannot be traded in. Ideally each person would have enough knowledge at least to be able to decide for themselves beforehand whether to run the risk of injury.

Paying for prevention

The idea that prevention is better than cure underpins all discussions on individual and public health. Paradoxically, however, insurance companies are reluctant to reimburse expenditure on prevention, usually confining their cover to treatment for injury, especially acute injury. This is short-sighted and will lead in the long run to higher treatment bills both for the individual and the nation. Investment in maintenance and development has to be more cost-effective than repeated repairs at high cost.

Evaluation of strategies

It is also difficult, although not impossible, to evaluate the outcome of prevention strategies in a scientific manner. So many different factors may cause injury that it is hard to single out the effect of any one factor with confidence. It is much easier to test an experimental treatment for a recognised disease. It has been suggested that this is why historically much more research money has been allocated to treatment than to prevention.[5]

Research into success of strategies

However, there is an encouraging study from Sweden, in which 12 soccer teams were divided into two groups, one being a control group and the other given a programme designed to prevent injuries. The programme consisted of a specially devised routine of warming up, cooling down and stretching; compulsory use of special training shoes and leg guards; instruction in preventive taping; individual rehabilitation programmes; weeding out players with chronically weak knees; education of coaches and players about the risks from faulty technique; and regular attendance at practice and games by the doctors and physiotherapists involved. Over a six-month period the test teams reported 75% fewer injuries than the control group.[6]

Importance of identifying individual strengths and weaknesses
Every body is different; genes, upbringing, body type, intelligence and capacity for work will vary. Some need to work physically six hours a day in order to improve performance, while others could achieve the same result in two. Some need more rest than others. What works for one person does not necessarily work for another. Sports coaches are beginning to accept that there are differences in physique, that not everyone can do everything, nor should they be forced to. Dance teachers, companies and performers have to learn to recognise the individual's physicality, to accept it and then to work with it. The teachers should be able to look at a **person**, not at a dance position. What is critical is to understand how the movement is done, in order to assess the correct and incorrect ways of doing it.

Developing appropriate fitness
Clearly one of the most important areas to be addressed, not only for injury prevention but also for improved all-round wellbeing, is that of developing appropriate fitness. Dance is reckoned to be second only to gymnastics in the demands it can make on all the components of physical fitness.[7] The Healthier Dancer Programme research has provided a baseline assessment of British dancers' fitness, although more long-term research needs to be done into the effectiveness of fitness training in preventing injuries. What is clear is that fitness training must be specific to the activity that is going to be performed. If the work calls for explosive bursts of power and acceleration, that is what the muscles must be trained for, plus adequate levels of cardiovascular endurance. If the choreography is less demanding, the level of cardiovascular endurance required will be correspondingly lower. Teachers,

choreographers and sports scientists will need to work together to devise and implement appropriate training programmes.

Reduction of repetitive movements

Sport recognises that it is usually physiologically counter-productive to keep on repeating movements beyond a certain point, so coaches learn to devise training programmes that vary the workload and thus the demands made on particular parts of the body. In dance, choreographers have been known to rehearse work to the point of exhaustion 'to see what it really looks like' or 'to get it right', which is clearly ineffective in the long run. The use of video in rehearsal is one way of helping choreographers to avoid this practice.

Working on both sides

Exercise should also be equally balanced on both sides of the body, in order to maintain true body alignment. There is already a high awareness in dance of the importance of good posture and body alignment, which is one of the reasons why many parents choose to send their children to dance classes. Class traditionally repeats movements on both sides. However, it would appear that some choreography works one side of the body more than the other. Where this is the case, there is a need to include work on the other side as a balance.

Muscular imbalance

Dance, particularly ballet, tends to work muscles in a particular pattern. This often means overworking one set of muscles (for example, muscles that point the foot) while underworking another set of muscles (for example, those that flex the foot). The turnout required for ballet demands extreme range of motion and strength for outward rotation only. This can create an imbalance in the muscles of the hip and lead to injury. Dancers will need to do additional exercises to correct these imbalances.

Importance of body conditioning

Sports physiotherapists are becoming very interested in the role of strong trunk muscles in providing a stable centre, so-called 'lumbar stabilisation'. A strong centre means much better postural alignment and should improve muscular imbalance. Traditional dance training concentrates on training the limbs and head, while neglecting the centre. This means that dancers often have very weak abdominal and lower-back muscles and do not learn how to strengthen them until they have been injured. Then they may well come across the Pilates technique, which has been substantially adopted and developed in the dance world. Its exact physiological effects are currently under study, but clinically it has proved a most useful tool in rehabilitation, particularly for patients with back problems. It is generally agreed that all dancers should have some idea of body conditioning from the beginning of their training and should not have to wait until they are injured. It is not even necessary to have available the full range of Pilates equipment, since many useful exercises can be done with just floor mats or even at the side of the stage while waiting to go on. It is of course important that such exercises are correctly taught in the first place.

CASE HISTORY 6

'S' works in South Asian dance. Before she started dancing much she injured her knee and when she began to dance seriously it became worse. Her NHS doctor told her that she would have to have surgery. A dancer friend suggested going to a physiotherapist who specialised in dance injuries although it would mean paying for treatment. The physiotherapist explained to her about strengthening the muscles around the knee and suggested that the Pilates technique might help. The Pilates practitioner taught her body mechanics and how to keep the body strong and supple. This made such a difference that she now starts every day in the rehearsal period with a body conditioning class.

'In South Asian dance people often learn the classical technique without much back-up in terms of body conditioning or a supplementary balanced exercise programme to put back what the dance takes out. The dancers I work with are always pleasantly surprised at how much their body awareness and stage performance are increased by such programmes.'

Usefulness of movement analysis

When the sports world looks at how best to prepare the athlete for extreme forms of exercise such as gymnastics or weightlifting, it is recognised that the aim has to be to maximise the benefits and minimise the risks. This is done by analysing very closely the exact requirements for top performance and tailoring a training programme to match each individual. Professional dance can also be extremely demanding, with the additional aesthetic requirement, but the results of such movement analysis as has been done are not widely known. Furthermore, dancers generally have less individual control of their schedule than athletes, do not know how to ease up if carrying an injury and are not yet encouraged to develop their own training programme.

Physical assessments at the beginning of the season or term

Leading professional football clubs now make their offer of a contract conditional on the player satisfactorily passing a full medical examination. With large sums of money involved for star players, the clubs need to be assured of the worth of their investment. Likewise, detailed physical assessments of dancers being taken onto new contracts or students being offered places at training schools could identify problem areas, muscle imbalances and areas of hypermobility, and examine the condition of the feet, degree of flexibility and muscle strength in the back, speed of reflexes and so on. Ideally this would again involve a multi-disciplinary team. Then where problems show up, the professionals can suggest corrective exercises for the individual dancer.

Importance of podiatry (footcare)

The use of podiatry is far more common in sport, which is surprising considering the number of foot and ankle injuries in dance. Many podiatrists use gait analysis as a diagnostic tool, using treadmills and video cameras. Dancers would probably be asked to perform a short movement sequence to be taped and analysed. Many injuries are caused or exacerbated by bad postural alignment, which can often be corrected by specially constructed inserts in the shoes; they do not necessarily have to be worn while dancing in order to be effective. When dancers are not doing class, for instance between rehearsals, they should wear a hard-soled shoe in order to maintain flexibility and proper muscle action. Dancers should do as many exercises for their feet as for other parts of the body, since it is so important that the feet be strong enough for the work being demanded. Many, however, appear to neglect foot exercises in their warm-ups and regular training routines. South Asian dance has long emphasised the importance of strengthening and caring for the feet, with the result that some of these dancers have the most mobile, expressive and strong feet.

New materials in pointe shoes

Much research and development work has been done in the last decade in the sports world to improve footwear. New materials and manufacturing techniques mean that there are now different shoes designed for different sports. Dancers on pointe have two long bones repetitively carrying five to six times the body weight on impact and are also asking the foot for a very wide range of motion. Yet the manufacturing techniques for pointe shoes have hardly changed this century. However, a company in New York has applied some of the new thinking about sports shoes to ballet pointe shoes (one of the partners is a retired professional dancer); initial results are encouraging but trials are still under way.

Floors

There has also been a lot of work on the best possible flooring surfaces for particular sports. Squash players' demands for better floors have led to the improvement of many courts over the last ten years. At the Lilleshall National Sports Centre, the purpose-built gym of the British Amateur Gymnastics Association (BAGA) has differently sprung surfaces for each of the various competitive disciplines. Thanks to BAGA's work in this area, even in local gymnastics clubs the floors are now much safer. Dancers often have to work on a variety of surfaces as they move from studio to studio, onto stage or in more unusual settings such as warehouses or streets. This is particularly a problem for the non-ballet dancer working in bare feet.

Dancing on hard, unyielding surfaces such as concrete or pavement can be dangerous to the lower limbs, maybe also the back. Placing a dance lino on a concrete surface, although better than nothing, does not greatly improve the situation. On the other hand, a too soft surface such as carpet gives no lateral stability, so the ankle is likely to roll over or be sprained. Ideally a dance floor should be resilient and also be capable of absorbing some of the shock when the dancer lands. The various kinds of portable and permanent floors that are suitable for dance have been discussed in much greater detail in Mark Foley's book.[8]

Raked stages

Dancing, walking or even standing on these inclined surfaces requires many adjustments in postural alignment and movement, which increases the stress on joints and muscles, as well as the risk of injury. This is particularly problematic for the dancer who has not trained on raked stages. A recent survey of Broadway dancers cited raked stages as a significant risk factor for dance injuries. As the authors say: 'Set designers should question whether somewhat improved audience viewing justifies more injuries. The results of this survey may not just apply to elite Broadway performers but can reasonably be generalised to include the great numbers of theatrical students and amateurs worldwide.'[9] It will be most interesting to see if the rake of the stage emerges as a significant factor in the survey of British dancers and actors in West End productions that is underway at the time of writing. The problem may be somewhat relieved by allowing sufficient practice and rehearsal time before performance and by incorporating into the dancer's routine special exercises designed to strengthen the muscles called into play in these different conditions.

Importance of rest

Sports medicine stresses the importance of scheduling rest periods as an integral part of a training plan, in order that the body has sufficient recovery time after hard physical activity. For some athletes, this means that as much time is scheduled for rest as for training. Some dancers in large companies may already be doing eight performances a week and one experienced dance physiotherapist suggested that this is already as much physical activity as the body can take. She noted that when extra rehearsals were called the rate of injury and illness increased dramatically. The myth is also still prevalent in dance that more than one day off will lead to a loss of skill, whereas in sport it is now accepted that no deterioration takes place until the end of three days at the very earliest and that one day off per week is essential. Teachers, trainers and administrators must therefore be prepared to think about changes in practice sessions and schedules. This approach has already been successful in Olympic-level sport. For instance, the Medical Officer to one of the English teams at the Barcelona Olympics scheduled two-hour rest periods in the afternoons, insisting on the athletes putting their feet up instead of shopping or sightseeing. The result was that there was a full eleven fit for each match and the team won the bronze medal. At the very least, dance could easily incorporate the use of relaxation techniques and stress the importance of a quick ten-minute nap in a quiet corner.

Sufficient sleep

Physiologists emphasise the importance of sleep in enabling the body to cope with the workload required. But dancers complain of disturbed sleep patterns from performing in the evening. Many dancers, particularly at the beginning of their career, find they are really wound up during the performance and that it is hard to dispel their heightened awareness after the show. First they need to find somewhere to eat and then they stay up late, going out to night-clubs or socialising. On tour, landladies are sometimes reluctant to allow their guests to sleep in, no matter how late their bedtime. In these circumstances, it is not surprising that dancers then find it very hard to work the next day, because the body has not had enough rest. Others find it hard to sleep when an important role is coming up, or start to worry about the lack of sleep itself. There are various techniques available to cope with these problems, which should be more widely known in dance.

Enhanced performance through good nutrition

The sports world has long recognised the importance of good balanced nutrition in enhancing performance and preventing injury. One of the major factors in dancers' injury is fatigue through under-eating, yet dancers are notorious for their poor diets. As one interviewee said: 'It's chocolate, cigarettes, Kit-Kats and Coke.' Many rely overmuch on fast food, being without the time, money, energy or confidence to cook for themselves. Some are trying to control their weight but have to cope with the myths still prevalent in the dance world, such as: 'food is the enemy'; 'carbohydrate makes you fat'; 'the best diet is high-protein, low-carbohydrate'.[10] The Healthier Dancer research showed that two-thirds of the dancers surveyed were taking supplements, most without any expert nutritional advice. As physically active people whose training begins at a young age and whose pattern of work requires them to keep at or near their peak for most of the year, dancers need to realise that food is fuel for work. They in fact need very specific nutritional advice. This is best provided during vocational training, but managements of companies, schools and theatres presenting dance need at the very least to ensure that any catering facilities offer a range of healthy options.

Importance of fluid intake

Dehydration is not widely appreciated to be another important factor in maintaining optimal physical performance and, perhaps, in injury prevention. Although so much of the human body consists of water, the loss of as little as 2% of body weight through sweating can adversely affect performance. Unlike sportspeople, dancers are not taught enough about the need to take in more fluid than the ordinary inactive person, relying only on the feeling of thirst to initiate fluid intake rather than taking in enough fluid before starting physical activity. Relying on thirst usually means drinking too little too late. There is also a widespread misconception that beer, lager, strong tea or coffee are good for replacing lost fluids.

Smoking

Sportspeople now understand that smoking impairs the cardiovascular system through the carbon monoxide in the inhaled smoke and therefore reduces their ability to become really fit. After all, just one cigarette temporarily reduces the oxygen carrying capacity of the blood by 2%. Smoking is also implicated as one of the factors in increased risk of osteoporosis and stress fractures. Very few elite athletes now smoke, and no endurance athletes. Many dancers, however, do. Moreover, the dangers of passive smoking are now clearly understood by most of the general population but there are still many areas of the dance world where non-smokers are subjected to this problem. This means a higher long-term risk of heart disease and many cancers for both smokers and non-smokers.

Substance abuse

Sport has done a great deal of work in detecting and researching the effects of different drugs on performance, from steroids to beta-blockers to common cold remedies. Clearly even recreational drugs interact with the physiology of the body; for instance the residues of marijuana are stored in the body fat for several weeks after inhalation and so will probably affect physical performance throughout that period. Very little is known about the current levels of substance abuse in dancers, although anecdotally it is said to be on the increase. More research is needed, but in the meantime dancers should be aware of the inherent dangers so that, again, they are able to take informed decisions.

Menstrual status

Young women doing strenuous physical activity should ideally still menstruate regularly. There are well attested links between restricted nutritional intake, intensive physical activity, the resulting amenorrhoea (lack of periods) and increased risk of osteoporosis (brittle-bone disease).[11] Already there are cases of female athletes in their 20s and 30s with osteoporotic fractures. The study by Victor Cross and Chris Boivin showed that professional ballet dancers with few, or no, periods had significantly lower bone density in the lower spine.[12] Even more worryingly, Dr Nicola Keay's work with retired ballet dancers found that those who had had fewest periods, or whose weight had dropped furthest below the ideal weight for their height, had the lowest spinal bone density. In some cases the bones had not recovered to the normal density for their age despite the resumption of normal periods.[13]

Experts think that probably all sportswomen should have three or four periods a year in order to reduce the risk to acceptable levels. If their periods are absent or irregular for more than six months, they should see a specialist in case there is a gynaecological problem and may have to consider some form of hormone replacement, even if this means simply taking the oral contraceptive pill. They should eat a calcium-rich diet, (i.e. with dairy products such as skimmed milk or yoghurt) particularly in their teen years, when the bone mass is building to its peak. Even if these risks seem far enough away to be discounted in the present, we know that stress fractures are definitely linked to inadequate nutrition and amenorrhoea, although the exact internal mechanism is not yet fully understood. Finally, the dancer with normal periods will recover more quickly from injury.

The use of psychology

There has been a small revolution in the appreciation of the role of psychology in enhancing performance and preventing injury in sport. Olympic athletes who have developed psychological skills such as anxiety control, concentration, motivation, interpersonal skills and so on, have been found to be better performers. These findings clearly indicate the importance of considering psychological skill training as an integral part of training the athlete to achieve optimal performance.[2] Even at the lower levels, coaches are now required to know about such topics as the role of the coach; group control; the use of praise and constructive criticism; task setting; evaluation and feedback; observation techniques; the role of demonstration as an aid to learning; visualisation and mental rehearsal.

In order to work with athletes at national or international level, coaches must understand factors affecting performance, such as anxiety, tension, fear and inappropriate thoughts; have an appreciation of stress and potential sources of anxiety, and a basic concept of the methods used to reduce anxiety; know how to prepare their athlete for performance through mental preparation and mental attitude; be able to teach performers to relax physically and mentally. Good dance teachers, of course, employ many of these methods, albeit for the most part unconsciously, but again these are skills which can be learned and improved with practice.

Development of support structures

Development of a national sports medicine structure

Efforts have already been made to pull the diverse strands of medical and
scientific knowledge together in the sports world. The National Sports
Medicine Institute (NSMI), set up by the Sports Council, plans to set up
15 regional Sports Medicine institutes in the UK in the next few years.
The standard module will incorporate an NHS hospital with Accident and
Emergency facilities; a sports injury clinic with a trained and experienced
sports doctor; links to a local university with a human performance
laboratory and sports scientists. Patients would have access to good
facilities and back-up services in psychology, stress management, nutrition,
all under one roof, while doctors would have regular access to patients
with sports injuries and be able to gain clinical experience. The need for
scientific facts rather than anecdotal evidence will be facilitated by the
immediate access to clinical data. The research will gain acceptance and
recognition for the centre's work in the medical and scientific community,
while the availability of treatment by sympathetic and experienced
practitioners should encourage the athletes to take part in the studies.

Development of a national performing arts medicine centre

Plans for an Institute of Performing Arts Medicine in central London are
still being formulated. This initiative comes from the British Performing
Arts Medicine Trust (BPAMT), set up to advance professional healthcare
for performing artists. Such an institute would provide clinical care for
actors, singers, musicians and dancers, as well as training opportunities
for doctors and physiotherapists, central coordination of information
and educational opportunities. This would act as an extremely valuable
catalyst for the many activities already in existence. It is to be hoped that
the negotiations currently under way with a major teaching hospital will
ultimately bear fruit.

Doctors appointed as medical advisers to orchestras

One of the achievements to date of BPAMT has been the creation of the
Association of Medical Advisers to British Orchestras (AMABO). This
scheme comprises a number of doctors appointed as honorary medical
advisers to the players in the regional orchestras and provides regular

training updates for its members. A good doctor is the first point of reference for the musicians and knows when and how to refer to other specialists. This model could well be applied to dance organisations.

Need to establish good communication

Health professionals working with organisations stress that both parties have to be prepared to spend time to establish a relationship of mutual trust. This will take time; one physiotherapist reported that it had taken 15 years for her organisation to ask her advice about what changes should be introduced, but now these are gradually being brought in. Dancers and dance companies should make efforts to educate health and sports professionals about their world, invite them to performances, credit them in programmes and generally try to engage their interest. There can then be a two-way flow of knowledge and information, to everyone's benefit. This structure should ideally be created from the start in order to encourage practitioners to work in this way and share information.

Networks for continuing exchanges of professional information

Several specialist groups have been set up in recent years to exchange information and encourage good practice in the treatment of elite athletes, such as the Sports Nutrition Foundation and the British Olympic Association's Psychology Advisory Group. In the same way, counsellors and physiotherapists working with performing artists are being encouraged to join the respective groups being organised by BPAMT.

International dissemination of information

In this respect, one of the most important organisations is the International Association for Dance Medicine and Science (IADMS). At the Association's annual conferences the latest research findings are presented, providing an excellent opportunity for professionals in the dance medicine and science and education fields to keep in touch with each other. In the meantime, BPAMT organises regular one-day seminars on a range of topics in performing arts medicine, to which overseas speakers and delegates are periodically invited. Mainly aimed at doctors and other health professionals, these often have direct relevance to dance or include specific examples from the dance world.

Training

Doctors' lack of knowledge

Currently, doctors often finish their training with little or no formal knowledge about exercise and fitness; for example, most are unaware that flexibility is an essential component of fitness and do not know how to examine a limb properly for flexibility. They also often have little opportunity during training to work with other health professionals such as physiotherapists or osteopaths. When they come to practise, doctors therefore do not fully appreciate the role of people trained in these disciplines, let alone the potential contribution of the complementary approaches.

The need for specific training of doctors

It is currently very difficult to train here in sports medicine because it is not yet recognised as a specialty in the medical profession. In this, Britain is behind many other European countries like Italy, Spain, Finland, Germany and Holland, as well as America and Australia. Attitudes are changing, however. The Royal Colleges are considering a proposal to set up an inter-collegiate Board of sports medicine and exercise science. In the long term this would mean that a doctor could decide to pursue an interest in sports medicine within the standard training framework, just as another could decide to specialise in Accident and Emergency work or paediatrics. Encouragingly, student doctors at the University of Glasgow Medical School can now do a BSc in sports medicine in their fourth year.

Becoming interested in sports medicine

In the meantime, practitioners are usually drawn into sports medicine because they have a personal interest in sport; after all, many doctors are themselves keen sportspeople in their spare time. Alternatively, they may happen to see a number of patients with sports-related problems and become interested in the field. Exactly the same applies to the field of performing arts medicine, where doctors may well have a personal interest in music, theatre or dance.

Current post-graduate training available

There are several post-graduate options currently open to the doctor who wishes to increase his or her knowledge of sports medicine. Apart from the one-year full-time Diploma course at the Royal London Hospital, there are various part-time courses such as those at the University of Nottingham, the University of Glasgow and the distance learning course provided by the University of Bath. The amount of clinical work required to complete these courses successfully, however, varies quite substantially and the syllabuses are very broad in nature, thus not allowing specialised study.

Acquisition of clinical experience

Even when the doctor has had some training in sports medicine, he or she needs to see enough sportspeople as patients to build up experience and expertise. Under the NHS this is increasingly difficult because of the heavy workloads. A few dedicated people soldier on inside the NHS, running specialised clinics with or without the backing and encouragement of their hospital managements; the danger is that the clinic would close if that particular individual were to move on. Many physicians interested in sports medicine end up going into private practice.

Provision of continuing education for doctors

It can be seen, then, that providing opportunities for doctors and other medically qualified people to keep up to date with specific treatments or problems in their field of interest is of paramount importance. Herein lies the value of the comprehensive education programme organised by the British Association of Sport and Medicine, open to GPs, physiotherapists, osteopaths, physicians and consultants. The treatment of dancers' injuries and their training are now included in the Intermediate course, which is to be welcomed. It may well be that in due time the impact of an Institute of Performing Arts Medicine will be similarly influential.

Training the trainers to incorporate safe practice

The problem of outdated knowledge being transmitted by coaches and trainers was recognised in the sports world some years ago. A number of

people realised that new methods were needed in order to improve
Britain's performance at Olympic level and that part of the solution lay
in improving the standard of coaching at all levels. Now, whatever his or
her sport, or level of experience, a coach can plug into the National
Coaching Foundation's inexpensive modular structure of home-based
learning and short courses in the evenings or at weekends. The
introductory courses are non-sports specific and cover basic anatomy
and physiology, principles of movement, sports psychology, planning
sessions, working with children and disabled sportspeople and
preventing and dealing with injuries. From there the coach can continue
training all the way through to a diploma at university level, gaining
National Vocational Qualifications (NVQs) throughout. Many
governing bodies run their own courses for coaches drawing on parts of
this framework, thus ensuring that there is a core curriculum familiar to
all their coaches, which can enhance the discipline-specific knowledge. It
should be possible to do the same in dance.

Dancers' and teachers' lack of health education

The need for good basic health education in dance has been repeatedly
stressed. Many dancers were taught very little during training about
good nutrition, safe use of the body, the need for scheduled rest and
ways to prevent injury. Some dancers then become teachers without any
formal training at all, but are supposed to be inherently good teachers
solely by virtue of being top performers. This used to be the situation in
sport, but it is now recognised that although top performers may possess
teaching skills, they are likely to be better at coaching other top
performers than at teaching people with less technical proficiency. At
whatever level, these skills need to be enhanced, practised and examined
before the teacher can truly be called professional.

In dance, even teachers with recognised qualifications may only have
had to demonstrate their ability to teach students how to pass syllabus
examinations. The focus has hitherto been on mastering technique.
Dance teachers may be masters in technique and artistic presentation,
but few have a thorough knowledge of human anatomy and kinesiology.
Although the situation is now changing, as the next chapter will show,
this leaves several generations of dancers and teachers without the

knowledge required to take sensible and informed decisions, or to teach safely in their turn, however good their mastery of technique. In order to ensure the overall safety of dance students, the examining bodies should be leading the way by insisting on their dance teachers having a better understanding of the body and dance-related health issues.

Finding time and money for skills enhancement

It is as well to remember, however, that few British sports coaches are paid for their coaching work. Most do it in their spare time. Dance teachers, on the other hand, have to earn their living from their teaching and may also be dancing or choreographing. For them, updating skills or acquiring new knowledge means not only finding the cost of the course but also taking time off work and possibly organising cover for their classes. In companies, dancers' schedules are often so crowded that there is little time for developing additional useful skills or catching up with the new knowledge. These are all problems to which the dance world must find positive solutions. The key is a change in attitudes.

References

1 Ann Bowling, 'Injuries to dancers: prevalence, treatment and perceptions of causes', *British Medical Journal*, vol. 298 (1989) pp. 731-4

2 Britt Tajet Foxell, 'The Management of Ballet Injuries', *Performing Arts Medicine News* (in press).

3 *Injuries in sport and exercise: a national study of the epidemiology of exercise-related injury and illness* (Sports Council, 1993)

4 Ruth Solomon, Lyle Micheli, John Solomon, and Tom Kelley, 'The "cost" of injuries in a professional ballet company: anatomy of a season', *Medical Problems of Performing Artists* (March 1995) pp. 3-10

5 Alice G Brandfonbrener, 'Prevention Strategies: Will they help or harm?' (Editorial), *Medical Problems of Performing Artists*, vol. 8 no 4 (December 1993)

6 Ekstrand et al, 'Prevention of soccer injuries', *American Journal of Sports Medicine*, vol. 11 no. 3, (1983)

7 Craig Sharp, 'The Physiology of the Dancer' in *The Healthier Dancer* (Laban Centre for Dance and Movement, 1991 reprinted 1995)

8 Mark Foley, *A Handbook for Dance Floors* (Dance UK, 1992)

9 Randolph Evans, Richard Evans, Scott Carvajal and Susan Perry, 'A Survey of Injuries among Broadway Performers', *American Journal of Public Health*, 86(10) (January 1996)

10 Myths dispelled in Tony Geeves' *The Safe Dance Report* (The Australian Association for Dance Education (Ausdance), 1990)

11 Roger Wolman, 'Amenorrhoea and osteoporosis in female endurance athletes, including dancers' in *The Healthier Dancer* (Laban Centre for Movement and Dance, London, 1991, reprinted 1995)

12 Victor Cross and Chris Boivin, 'Bone density and injury in ballet dancers', *Dancing Times* (September 1995) pp. 1187-9

13 Nicola Keay, 'Dancers, periods and osteoporosis', *Dancing Times* (September 1995) p. 1189

Dancer: Darshan Singh Bhuller: Richard Alston Dance Company
Photograph: Anthony Crickmay

7

What the dance world can do

WHAT THE DANCE WORLD CAN DO

The need for change
Whether in subsidised or commercial theatre, there is much that is excellent in British professional dance. How else could the present standard of performance be sustained? At the same time our research shows how much there is to put right. Evidence lies in the level of injuries in all styles of dance; in our research on fitness, nutritional status and psychological aspects; in supplementary evidence from abroad, especially from Australia and the USA; in the report from Dance UK's conference on training professional dancers; in individual interviews with students in vocational schools and professional dancers in companies or working freelance; and finally in dancers' own lifestyles. Sources are listed in Appendix D. However, our information regarding the situation in other countries mostly concerns the large companies. This is partly because, as in the UK, they are the ones principally experiencing the daily pattern of injury and facing the need to control costs. They also have the ability to access resources and to make changes. We have chosen to quote substantial professional opinion with a view to identifying the areas for further research, but would make no claim to have carried out a full audit of good practice, either in Britain or overseas.

A re-think required
These findings imply a re-think of traditional dance training. It does not mean scrapping historical methods. What it does mean is that when this experience was codified by Carlo Blasis and August Bournonville in the 19th century, the dance world and lifestyles were very different from today. Even when supplemented by Enrico Cecchetti and other great teachers in our own time, the training and attitudes inherited from the past are unable to satisfy the demands of late 20th century dance. **Not only choreographic demands but touring demands, performance demands and the stress of life generally call for a different approach to training today.**

Impact of change
Change itself and the need for more change are acknowledged throughout the dance world. It was the theme and recommendation of

Dance UK's international conference on training professional dancers in September 1993. That conference and its predecessor, *The Healthier Dancer* in 1990, emphasised the need for closer liaison between dance and sports science as a means of achieving change. Hindered by lack of finance and nurtured in tradition, companies, dancers and schools move slowly to effect change. No British dance company or school at the moment is allowed enough resources to apply all the discoveries of sports science. For the vocational schools, struggling for survival and coping with the problems of the reduction in discretionary grants, it is perhaps hardly surprising that the incorporation of good practice remains a particular challenge. In any organisation, not only the board of management and financial controllers need to be persuaded, but dancers and students themselves, and often the funding bodies. Even so, we have found many changes for the better since the 1960s.

Classical ballet then
Thirty years ago floors were harder, rehearsal spaces and stages damper and colder. Dancers needed to be aware of holes and other dangers in stages, even at the Royal Opera House. There was much less central heating. Physiotherapists experienced in dance were few, all in private practice and all in London. Counselling and psychological help were the exception. No-one appreciated the importance of cooling down as well as warming up. Overseas tours were very long, involving many one-night stands and much stress. To tour in the UK was to experience poorly heated, uncomfortable lodgings, cold rehearsal rooms, theatres with no hot water and unreliable train journeys. In these conditions, no-one thought it unusual that dancers often retired after a few years.

The situation today
Because of increased knowledge, today's dancers in the large companies expect, rightly, to pursue a long career with support throughout. They expect on-site physiotherapy and professional massage. They expect to be prepared in advance for hazards like raked stages, unusually difficult venues or a particularly demanding repertory requiring special training.

If dancers leave a company after two or three years, it is often to expand careers in other directions rather than because of chronic injury. Above all there is a growing realisation that dancers have minds as well as bodies and that the mind of the dancer needs nurturing as much as the body. In ballet, for example, it is too easy to be locked into dance from the age of eight with few chances of wider experience or personal enrichment. Yet there have been some advances within the last few years in developing dancers as individuals along the same lines as athletes.

Focus on individual development in independent dance

In fact, many of the independent dancers see their life's work as developing and refining their own individual style in a way that is sensitive and suitable to their own bodies in order to communicate better with the audience. Each piece of work is a further exploration of individual skills (both mental and physical), aptitudes and personalities, often welded together by the choreographer working as a team leader rather than as the more traditional sole source of dance material and ideas. There are no rules; in some smaller companies the choreographer plays a traditional director's role, but with an understandably closer relationship to the individual dancers because fewer people are involved.

Interest in body therapies

Because of this approach to developing the individual's mind and body to the maximum potential, many independent dancers are naturally drawn to the explorations of what are called the 'body therapies'. Here the body and mind are seen as indivisible, capable of development only if the two work in conjunction and harmony with each other. This encompasses a number of approaches from both the East (such as the martial arts, yoga, t'ai chi, Shiatsu) and the West (for example Alexander Technique, Feldenkrais, autogenics, structural integration, ideokinesis, body-mind centering). With this interest, it is not surprising that many independent dancers, if injured, choose to turn first to complementary therapies for treatment.

Improving physical fitness

Examples from smaller companies

As part of their explorations, some independent dancers and companies have recognised the need to bring in outside experts to help develop their physical fitness, perhaps for a particular production or as an all-round performance enhancement. For example, Motionhouse, a company based in the Midlands, has worked for many years with a local gym to devise appropriate training packages. Dancers start the day with a good warm-up and an aerobic session before class and also follow individual weight-training programmes. On tour, one of the artistic directors leads the other dancers in running round a football pitch, with appropriate shoes supplied as part of a sponsorship deal. The results: increased stamina and capacity to deal with the workload, manifested clearly during auditions in late 1995, when the auditionees felt they had had a really hard day while the company members were still fresh.

Companies such as DV8 and V-Tol perform work that makes great physical and mental demands. Like many independent dancers, V-Tol's members all swim, as well as doing fitness training in company time. On two days a week company class is replaced with training for strength, stamina or explosive power, perhaps with a few endurance exercises, and rehearsal time includes playing a lot of games that develop various aspects of fitness. DV8 always insist on dancers beginning a rehearsal period with a good basic level of fitness which can then be overlaid with training specific to the work being created, such as rope work and Irish dancing in the production of *Enter Achilles*.

Fitness training in the larger companies

The picture is patchier in the larger companies, where a major problem is the organisation of time to accommodate an exercise programme appropriate to the repertory. This problem must be resolved if prevention of injury is to take precedence over repairing injury. Much depends upon the attitude of the artistic director, teachers and rehearsal staff. Problems in teaching arise from a mismatch between training and the work to be done, and resistance to the introduction of supplements such as body training machines. Many teachers reject these supplements in the mistaken belief that traditional training is adequate in itself. Then it is left to the determination of the individual dancer. At the *Fit to Dance?* conference in October 1995, Deborah Bull, a principal artist with the Royal Ballet, reported how her personal fitness programme has immensely improved her stamina and endurance, making it possible to complete a demanding Forsythe ballet without being exhausted.[1] Many of her colleagues in the company, however, are yet to be convinced, although they have off-peak access to a local gym.

Company initiatives

Some of the men in the Birmingham Royal Ballet have taken part in strength training programmes with Dr Yiannis Koutedakis and found that their ability to lift their partners has increased. Many of the dancers have taken up swimming on a regular basis, while some may join the early morning aerobic sessions available for the rest of the staff. Dancers in the former London Contemporary Dance Theatre did a lot of fitness work, particularly before demanding pieces such as *Troy Game*. Mats and a set of free weights went out on tour in the company van so that the dancers could keep up their schedules while away from base. Phoenix Dance Company dancers, involved in a tailored fitness training programme initiated by the artistic director, now regularly visit the gym and are showing good improvements in fitness. In general, however, without more positive encouragement from the company managements, this progress will continue to be uneven and to rely substantially on individual initiative.

Fitness programmes in schools

There are many noteworthy developments in the schools. Royal Ballet School students are encouraged to skip or cycle regularly, while the male students at the English National Ballet School are now regularly taken on running sessions by one of the head teachers, himself a marathon runner. The new School has an on-site gym. London Contemporary Dance School students are now beginning to follow individual regimes, as well as attending formal lectures on dance physiology and fitness both at undergraduate and postgraduate level. Some students might like to improve fitness, but find it hard to know where to begin or where to find the time or space to incorporate the sessions into their schedules, which are even more rigorously timetabled and controlled than those of the professional dancers. It must also be remembered that nowadays cuts in funding mean that students often have to take part-time jobs outside their school time in order to earn the money for their courses.

Graduated workloads

Dancers have to learn that achieving fitness must be part of their individual responsibility and that they should return from holiday or start a new contract with a basic level of fitness. We then need to learn in dance from sport practice, in which graduated workloads can achieve peak physical performance. Dance companies and schools, under financial and psychological pressures to show results in a short time and understanding less well the process of gradual adaptation to training, too often start dancers and students at the beginning of term or a new season in flat-out schedules, which increases the risk of injury. Some organisations, such as the Royal Ballet companies and Central School, schedule a lighter workload in the first week back from a break. In the independent sector, however, a group may have only six weeks to produce a new work from start to finish. This time period is clearly insufficient to train for particularly demanding work, which is why companies such as DV8, V-Tol and Motionhouse insist on longer rehearsal periods. However, this does pose problems of resources. Practical investigation is required into how the concept of a graduated workload could be applied more widely in dance practice.

Class

There is still great confusion about the purpose of class. Many dancers still believe it is a warm-up, although it will not act as one unless specifically designed to do so. Indeed, many classes are so immediately demanding that an extremely thorough warm-up **beforehand** is required. Class is by no means adequate fitness training, because the workload is not specific enough to train the different fitness parameters, nor is it graduated, nor tailored to individual need. Experience suggests that class is where the dancer learns and refines skill. It should help to focus attention on correct technique and prepare the dancer for the work ahead. There is a need to

recognise that class will have a different purpose for the recreational
dancer, the student in vocational training and the professional dancer.

Company class

It seems sensible that company class should as far as possible be
appropriate to the existing repertoire and to the repertoire being brought
in. This is the thinking behind Netherlands Dance Theatre's move to a
mixture of ballet and contemporary classes. Some have suggested that
company class in a rehearsal period should be different from that during
a run of performances. Others have suggested that for some dancers six
classes a week is too unvarying and may even be counter-productive. It is
certainly time to dispel the myth that 'the more classes, the better',[2]
irrespective of the rest of the timetable and the dancer's level of fitness.
However, there is no straightforward relationship between volumes of
work and ultimate performance; it will be different for each person.

Warm-up

None of the above considerations precludes the necessity for a proper
warm-up, with its constituent elements of increase in internal muscle
temperature and breathing rate, mobilisation of the joints and short
stretches of the major muscle groups. Commercial managements identify
the failure of dancers to take class as a major cause of injury, but it may
be that the problem is as much the failure to warm up properly. Some
dancers working in musical theatre do not even take advantage of the
free company warm-up before the show. Managements are considering
imposing a penalty on those who persistently fail to attend. Yet dancers
interviewed said that they often find the pre-show warm-up too
unvarying and too undemanding, either physically or mentally. If there
are complicated costumes or make-up to attend to before the show, the
body might well lose the benefits, which usually dissipate after 30
minutes, and have to be warmed up again. There is surely room here for
some sensible discussion. All dancers have to be self-disciplined, a
quality which should be instilled in initial training, in order to devise
and follow their own individual training routine, appropriate to their
body and their needs. This is particularly important when performing in
the same show night after night.

Research required

Much more research is needed into the demands made on the body by dance, but it would certainly seem urgent to devise warm-up programmes specific to the various styles. This topic has sparked discussion in the South Asian dance field, where the concept of warm-up is relatively new, so much so that a 1995 publication on teaching South Asian dance in schools included two pages on warm-up and cool-down.[3] For the same reasons, similar research is required into the demands of both traditional and non-traditional Afro-Caribbean dance.

Access to body control work

Several schools have brought in body control teachers on a regular basis; at the Arts Educational School in Tring all dancers from the age of eight begin their day with 40 minutes of body conditioning, while the summer schools of both the National Ballet School of Canada and the School of American Ballet have begun to incorporate a session of body conditioning at the beginning of each day. The Shobana Jeyasingh Company, with work as physically demanding as any professional Western dance, begin each day during the rehearsal period with body conditioning classes. Some schools and companies have installed Pilates equipment, deciding that this technique is too valuable to be left to the individual initiative of dancers. Then the problem can arise of properly qualified supervision; in some places the equipment has to lie unused for periods because of lack of money to pay trained staff for more than a few sessions a week. This perhaps highlights the problem of its being often easier to raise money for equipment than for people.

Physical assessments: schools

Schools such as the Royal Ballet School and the Dance School of Scotland ask an orthopaedic consultant or a physiotherapist to undertake a screening of applicants who have passed the first audition and prepare a detailed written assessment to help in the final decision-making process. Students applying for discretionary grants for a course accredited by the Council for Dance Education and Training are given a physical examination and detailed written report as part of the assessment process. At the Arts Educational School in Tring students have regular assessments which look at muscular imbalances, strengths and weaknesses. In Israel, Jeannette Ordman, the founder of the Bat Dor Company, has worked closely with the director of the country's first dance medicine centre to institute compulsory physical screenings at all auditions for the Bat Dor School and summer school. The resulting individual reports, detailing overall suitability for professional dance, are given not only to the teacher, but also to the students and their parents.

Physical assessments: companies
Companies might like to insist on knowing the physical history of potential dancers, but schools are sometimes reluctant to divulge the information for fear of prejudicing the students' job opportunities. In America, however, where all companies have by law to pay medical insurance for their dancers, some seasonal companies, finding that the majority of claims were being filed in the first and last months of employment, are now instituting physical screenings during auditions to identify potential or chronic injuries before making final hiring decisions. In Britain both the Richard Alston Dance Company and the Really Useful Company pay for a full medical on newcomers, including a fitness assessment from a physiotherapist.

Lifestyle issues

Food
There is widespread agreement that this is mainly a matter for individual decision-making, but that a dancer must be able to make informed choices. Knowledge about healthy eating and proper fluid intake is still surrounded with myth and tradition in the dance world. This has to be addressed in training. The Royal Ballet School, the Royal Academy of Dancing teachers' training course and Central School have all brought in guest lecturers. However, one-off sessions are not enough to change ingrained eating patterns. Some schools still weigh students publicly and some artistic directors still apply a weight standard. These practices have to go. Too many cafeterias still provide an array of tempting sweet foods, sugary drinks and colas rather than healthy choices. When moving into their new premises, the Birmingham Royal Ballet was able to insist on a full range of healthy

food being available in its own cafeteria, but most dancers have to rely on facilities provided and controlled by other people.

Fluid intake

Matters would appear to have improved somewhat since *The Healthier Dancer* conference in 1990. The scientific view that people who are well hydrated perform better is more generally understood. Students are now encouraged to take water bottles in to RAD examinations. Many dancers are now to be seen walking around with large bottles of still water, although some individuals nevertheless complain about feeling bloated. They need to learn the technique of taking small, regular sips. Rambert Dance Company went so far as to provide all their dancers with water bottles such as are used by racing cyclists in order to emphasise the importance of adequate hydration, as well as to reduce the risk of water backstage coming into contact with electrical cables.

Smoking

With the recent award of large damages for passive smoking to a public sector employee, strict no-smoking policies are now in force in all tertiary education institutions. On the other hand, it sometimes feels as if the dance world is the last bastion of tobacco. Dancers do not appear to realise that it has now been scientifically established that smoking immediately after physical activity is particularly bad because a larger proportion of the smoking-related substances are trapped in the body, with more severe consequences. The Birmingham Royal Ballet and the Laban Centre, however, have recently initiated no-smoking policies and English National Ballet has taken advantage of the extra space made available by the move of the School to designate clear smoking and non-smoking areas. At the RAD College the students themselves requested a no-smoking common room three years ago. Some dancers report that they begin smoking only upon arriving at school, partly to cope with the unfamiliarity and pressure, partly because it is socially acceptable and partly to suppress appetite.

Working conditions

Touring problems

Huge dangers arise on tour. Replacement casts need as careful
preparation as first casts, but often never receive it. (We have evidence,
even today, of dancers being pushed into an emergency performance of a
new role with little preparation.) In these circumstances, the risk of
injury is maximised. Then there is the regular problem on tour of
dancers getting cold because of conditions in the theatre where they
have to work. Floors are another problem, sometimes on steel,
sometimes on concrete, threatening the dancers' muscles and a well-
known factor in stress fractures. In Britain particularly, it is known that
touring facilities, touring allowances and overnight accommodation are
all below standard, yet for years dancers have made little protest. The
situation has been exacerbated by demands from the arts funding bodies
for what is generally considered to be an excessive number of touring
weeks, fortunately now being reduced through negotiation. However,
the problems of inadequate touring allowances and poor
accommodation still have to be tackled. Funding bodies cannot be
absolved of their share of responsibility for overcrowded touring
schedules and demands for new productions, often necessitating extra
rehearsals on tour in ill-equipped spaces.

Environmental conditions

There are still far too many hard floors in theatres and studios
throughout Britain and many community dancers have to work week in,
week out on concrete surfaces. Few dancers enjoy purpose-built premises
such as are available for the Birmingham Royal Ballet, with properly
sprung floors and good ventilation. Having the benefit of a superb stage
and rehearsal facility at its home base, BRB is now fighting to change
conditions in some of the British touring theatres, where hard floors,
lack of rehearsal space, poor ventilation and heating, all contribute to
increased risk of injury once on tour, even in some quite prestigious
venues. In a move to improve conditions, the Council of Dance
Education and Training's revised procedures for accrediting courses in
vocational schools now assess in some detail every studio used on the

course. The advent of the National Lottery should make a considerable difference to the fabric of many of our touring theatres and studios, but none of these improvements will come about without continual pressure; dancers from overseas are often shocked at the conditions that British dancers are prepared to accept.

Problems particular to musical theatre

Unlike their American counterparts, dancers in the UK have not in the past moved easily between commercial and subsidised dance theatre. Because the situation is changing and choreographers in commercial theatre are producing choreography that is attractive to all dancers, injury problems may arise because of the lack of specific training. There may also be problems from the particular circumstances of commercial theatre such as repetition of the same movements night after night for eight shows a week, the prevalence of raked stages or the weight of elaborate head-dresses. (Of course, they may also derive from dancers and their lifestyle: the failure of dancers, for example, to assume responsibility for warming up properly, taking regular class, eating properly and getting enough sleep.)

One problem in musical theatre is a lack of backstage space for warming up or trying out new movements. Insufficient attention is paid to the springing of floors or to temperature levels. Some commercial theatres, built in the 19th century, still do not have proper temperature controls and are very cold in winter. Sometimes there are clashes between dancers and singers which need refereeing by managers; singers complain about the effect on their voices if the air is too hot or too dry. Sometimes there are not enough icepacks and water bottles for dancers during a show or inadequate catering arrangements.

Injury management

Developing procedures in companies

It has been a long struggle to persuade managements to meet the cost of injury. Today large companies must pay full salary for an agreed number of weeks and the full cost of treatment. Even so, this often applies only if the injury occurs during working hours. Because of the high costs

involved, these managements are only too well aware of the need for
prompt, appropriate injury treatment and proper rehabilitation
programmes. They realise that it is more cost-effective in the long run
for the dancer to return quickly and safely from injury. Procedures differ
between managements, but generally an injured dancer is referred at
once to a physiotherapist, of either the management's or the dancer's
choosing. The physiotherapist then treats the dancer or makes onward
referral to a hospital emergency department or a specialist. With the
dancer's permission, the company is given a written report. Since
arrangements of this kind are relatively recent, some managements are
generous, some much less so. Generosity, whatever the level, is a
response partly to union pressure, partly to the development of more
challenging choreography. Many difficulties remain to be overcome
before there are widely agreed procedures for effective dancer health and
injury care.

Immediate treatment for injury

As mentioned in chapter 4, the management survey showed that several
large companies now have systems in place designed to deal with injury
as soon as it happens. This is true of some schools as well. The Royal
Ballet companies and the Royal Ballet School have employed chartered
physiotherapists and built or converted special treatment rooms. In a
move designed to improve knowledge and information about dancers'
injuries, all dancers must now first be assessed by the physiotherapist
before any treatment can be authorised, even if the dancer then decides
to go to an outside therapist. Statistical services are being created to
record injuries systematically. Other companies and schools, such as
Rambert, English National Ballet, the Laban Centre and Elmhurst Ballet
School, have made arrangements for regular visits from physiotherapists,
while Central School has in addition paid for some sessions with
complementary therapists. Arts Educational School in Tring has made a
dedicated treatment room available for the visiting physiotherapist and
massage therapist, as well as setting up a limited fund for students who
need treatment but are unable to pay for it. London Contemporary
Dance Theatre used to bring in an osteopath for a day a week to check
out all the company members, in a move which showed a realisation of

the importance of preventative work alongside remedial. However, no British company insists on doctors or physiotherapists being present at every performance, as has become more common practice with teams in the sports world. Overseas, Philip Morris funded the Harkness Center for Dance Injuries to provide a doctor in attendance at every New York performance of the Joffrey Ballet and the Alvin Ailey Company.

Paying for treatment

The other ballet companies and commercial managements rely on immediate treatment being made available in outside facilities, either through paying private medical insurance premiums or by raising sponsorship from a healthcare provider, as Scottish Ballet has done. Schools without regular physiotherapy arrangements suggest that students must have private medical insurance cover, either under their parents' policy or via the school; in some instances the cost of premiums is added to fees that, being unsubsidised, are already extremely high.

Problems of injury management on tour

Only the larger companies can afford to take their physiotherapists on tour. Other companies, such as Northern Ballet Theatre and touring West End productions, have had to establish their own network of experienced and sympathetic practitioners in each city visited over the years. Overseas touring presents particular problems. Since none of the companies is allowed to use subsidy to support foreign work, they have to work to extremely tight budgets and usually have to rely on travel insurance when they go overseas. Lack of access to physiotherapy leaves the dancers particularly vulnerable to the possibility of a niggling injury developing into a full-grade problem. It also places an inappropriate burden of healthcare onto the company manager or other staff, for which they may not be properly qualified.

Health and Safety

The Council for Dance Education and Training now ask vocational schools applying for accredited course status to state their health and safety policy, which should include a blood spillage and HIV awareness policy. Information on first aid provision, nutrition, physiotherapy, body conditioning and counselling services are also requested and examined as part of the accreditation procedures. Most companies are aware of their responsibility as employers to have adequate numbers of trained First Aiders; some have now trained not only office staff but also stage managers or artistic staff who go out on tour. English National Ballet has developed a particular emphasis on health and safety for all employees within its personnel policy. This includes company pension and health insurance schemes, the identification of safety responsibilities at all levels, First Aid training, protection of display screen users and an HIV/AIDS policy that embraces education for all employees and guarantees confidentiality. Other companies, of course, have similar policies. This example indicates that the necessary experience already exists within professional dance. Organisations without such policies should endeavour to put matters right as soon as possible.

Smaller companies and independents

For the most part, the smaller companies and independent dancers do not have the resources to organise adequate provision against illness or injury. Through membership of Dance UK, however, they do have access to an accident insurance scheme and to a register of health practitioners with experience of working with dancers. The management questionnaires reveal a situation in which these companies directly experience few problems with injury and therefore feel little need for more health cover, especially when current resources do not permit adequate salaries. Those working on the Independent Theatre Council's Equity contract have to pay sick pay for a certain number of weeks and would normally make some contribution towards sessions with therapists, but the others are unlikely to have even a small medical budget.

Effects of injury in this sector

However, should a dancer working for one of these companies fall ill or sustain an injury, the effect on the dancer and on the company can be quite catastrophic. Without private medical insurance, the dancer has to turn to the NHS for help or find medical costs, sometimes substantial, from his or her own pocket. The temptation is not to seek treatment at all. The pressure to continue to perform on the injury and not to let the company down, is very great. If the injury is too severe for the dancer to struggle on, the rest of the group will try to cope by re-working the choreography for fewer numbers. The better-resourced companies will try to keep the injured dancer on the payroll but in many cases the dancer will be thrown back onto State benefits (currently less than £60 a week).

CASE HISTORY 7

'G' works in contemporary dance, has always tried to take care of her body, and encourages others to do the same. While teaching a two-week workshop abroad she had to work in extremely cold spaces, with no heating. She felt a pull deep in her pelvis but could not get immediate treatment. On her return to Britain she had to go straight into rehearsals for a new piece with a small company. In class she mis-timed a move, felt something 'go' and seized up, so that she could barely walk. Her regular therapist was away and another therapist she saw was unable to diagnose the problem. In rehearsal now she was only 'marking' but still felt pain and immobility. The company then went on an overseas tour. She got through one performance but was then unable to move and spent several days teaching her material to over-worked colleagues.

Back in Britain 'G' consulted several therapists without satisfaction until she found an expensive one who did a thorough investigation and suggested an X-ray. Although there was a delay in getting an appointment, her GP was helpful about getting the X-ray done at the local hospital. It then took three weeks for the radiologist's written report to come through, by which time the treatments had cost 'G' a lot of money. Fortunately the company agreed to pay her full salary through to the end of the contract, although there was no money in the budget for such a contingency.

'Never having been off work before, it was difficult to make the decision not to perform. Going back, I felt a slight loss of nerve despite every support from the company. If you normally work in good conditions and go into bad, it can be really hard to adapt. And unless a therapist already knows your body well, it is hard for them to assess an acute situation.'

Importance of appropriate rehabilitation

In the event of injury an individual plan of action for each dancer should be prepared. At the Royal Ballet, this is part of a formal rehabilitation structure, which accepts that every dancer needs to proceed at a different pace. In particular, building on the pioneer work of Winifred Edwards and Joan Lawson, two creative teachers with exceptional knowledge of dancers' anatomy and physiology, there is acceptance of the need for regular, daily remedial work, as initiated and developed by Monica Mason, the Assistant Director.[4,5] This work not only helps dancers return to work more safely from injury but takes into account human situations like pregnancy, or causes of injury like ill-fitting pointe shoes.

An example from America

At San Francisco Ballet a new company doctor found that the insurance premiums were over $1 million a year despite two on-site physiotherapists. He persuaded the company to pay directly for complementary treatments such as osteopathy; this system reduced paperwork and speeded up treatment. An ex-dancer himself, he began to teach a rehabilitation class, modelled on the normal company class, to ease dancers back into work. All this paid off in a 50% reduction rate in injuries between his first and second seasons.

A coordinated approach to healthcare at the Boston Ballet

Partly impelled by the need to reduce insurance premiums, Boston Ballet drew up a programme designed to address the problems of dancers' healthcare. Driven by the Artistic Director, Bruce Marks, and the Board, the new programme has included on-site physiotherapy; lectures on injury prevention; separate remedial classes given jointly by a teacher and one of the physiotherapists; attendance at each performance by a doctor and physiotherapist. A move into new premises permitted the provision of a weight-training room with body conditioning equipment; an instructor comes in on a regular basis in order to supervise correct use of the equipment. There is a healthcare education agenda item at each Board meeting since it is the directors who are charged with raising funds for the continuation of the programnme.

Dancers are encouraged to report potential problems sooner rather than later so that symptoms can be treated before they become an injury. 'One twinge and they're upstairs.' The company has more cost control, since dancers no longer visit therapists all over the city and injuries are reported earlier on. Most encouragingly, the injury rate has dropped markedly. The Artistic Director has also taken action to improve practice within the Boston Ballet School, explaining to the teachers the reasoning behind the banning of such practices as insisting on 180° turnout, or physically forcing arms and legs into extreme positions. There is now a consistency of training between students in each year and the company, as well as access to stress management counselling.

Psychological issues

The need to keep injured dancers involved in the dance community

It is evident that a dancer's recovery from injury is much affected by the atmosphere in which that recovery takes place. While it is understandable that the first reaction of artistic directors and staff on learning of an injury is annoyance, perhaps even anger, it is essential that this feeling is not communicated to the dancer. This involves creating a climate of support around the injured person. With small companies, the injured dancer will probably be required to teach his or her part to another member of the company and so will be unlikely to become socially isolated and depressed. In larger companies, a more concerted effort has to be made to ensure that an appropriate support system is in place. In some commercial productions, injured dancers are expected to attend rehearsals and watch shows, as long as mobility permits, because the importance of treating them as an integral part of the cast is fully appreciated. At Boston Ballet the staff have learnt that their attitude to the injured dancer is critical. 'There must be no punishing for illness.' (Bruce Marks in interview). An injured dancer who is mobile has the opportunity to decide what modified duty to perform; thus he or she is kept working and still feels involved with the organisation.

Relaxation, pacing and staleness

A few companies and artists have started to realise the importance of incorporating rest periods into their schedule. Diversions Dance

Company, for example, has taken a policy decision not to work on Saturdays during the rehearsal period, while V-Tol try normally to take a two-hour lunch break in the middle of the day, both to allow the dancers to eat a properly balanced meal and to have time to digest it before starting work in the afternoon. The second hour of the break is then available for discussion or company meetings. Phoenix Dance Company took the risk of giving the dancers the day off before opening a new production and were pleasantly surprised to report a much higher energy level and no injuries. At Netherlands Dance Theatre a new dance fitness therapist discovered that the injury rate was running at such a level that an alarming 50% of dancers should probably not have been working. Working closely with the company's orthopaedic specialist, he persuaded the company that many of the dancers were over-tired and should as a matter of urgency have an extra week's holiday.

Relaxation techniques

We have seen that many independent dancers are already exploring the potential of alternative ways of working with the body as part of their personal development as a dancer. To some extent this has begun to feed back into training, especially in those schools teaching contemporary dance. At the Laban Centre one of the lecturers, teaching anatomy and Pilates work, has also qualified as a teacher of the Alexander Technique and gave a presentation on the topic at a staff conference. Much more work needs to be done before relaxation and rest are built into training schedules as a normal part of dance activity.

Access to counselling

Progress on the psychological front has been much slower than on the physical, but some tentative steps have been taken. Vocational schools with boarding students under the age of 18 must by law have a student counsellor available; Central School, although not taking boarders, has gone a step further by putting a trained psychologist on staff part-time, with complete confidentiality assured for individual or group sessions. At the Royal Ballet regular counselling is now available from a trained occupational psychologist, Britt Tajet-Foxell, who has adapted sports psychology techniques, such as the use of positive visualisation to overcome fear of difficult movements, or goal-setting to cope with the special problems of returning from injury. She has organised a series of lectures on the role of psychology in ballet for The Royal Ballet School teachers' course.

Career planning

One recent initiative has been the piloting of an induction package for new entrants to the Royal Ballet, which encourages them to take an active role in learning their way around the organisation and its many facets. The follow-up has unfortunately fallen victim to funding cuts, but the valuable experience thus gained is feeding into a BAPAM project on developing guidelines for induction packages in schools and companies. Some schools have also begun to develop the ideas of personal career planning. At the School of American Ballet a career seminar included talks from two professional ballet dancers on life in a ballet company, a psychologist and counsellor specialising in transition, and a representative of the dancers' union to give an overview of the economics of dance. One other school cited in the recent *Classical Ballet Training Study* commissioned by Dance/USA sends out a prospectus to parents which lists a large number of career options in dance open to their graduates: 'Performer is in the middle of the list, under "p".'[6] At Central School each new entrant has to draw up his or her own career plan, with encouragement and advice available from staff as required. These plans are then reviewed and, if necessary, modified at regular intervals throughout the student's training. Final-year students at London Contemporary Dance School have a week of sessions on career planning, self-management and the skills necessary to forge a career in today's dance world. Although these once-only sessions are valuable, we should remember that the students interviewed suggested that these topics ideally needed more time and should be built into the final-year timetable. Many schools are still resistant to even the notion of introducing discussions about later career options.

Improvements in psychological approaches

Much work needs still to be done so that teachers can be sure that they are giving corrections and encouragement in the best way and students can be coached to give their best work. At the Arts Educational School in Tring students are now encouraged to question their training, to use visualisation, to improvise in short sections using ballet steps and to take responsibility for their own learning. This approach is being closely evaluated. At the Boston Ballet School teachers have come to accept the observation of their work, to encourage feedback and understand that the school will take action if the teaching does not improve. Every week all faculty staff participate in a session, led by the principal, on the 'why' of teaching, rather than the 'how'. Netherlands Dance Theatre's dancers have an optional class every morning incorporating various physical and mental techniques, such as yoga, mental focusing and preparation. These are pioneer steps indeed, but vital to ensure the present, and future, emotional health of dancers and students.

Training

Developing links with health professionals

Since it takes time to become experienced in treating dancers, it well behoves the dance world to make efforts to develop appropriate and effective systems of communication with sympathetic practitioners, rather than leaving progress to the initiative of a few committed individuals. At the Arts Educational School in Tring, for example, a team of healthcare professionals is being brought together to advise the school on how best to minimise injuries and promote positive health. The information thus gleaned is disseminated to other teachers through in-service training, lectures, demonstrations and articles in the press.

Developments in Australia

From the two Dance UK conferences[4,7] and the findings of the Safe Dance Report,[2] we know that companies have introduced a variety of injury prevention techniques: a graduated workload after return from holidays; seminars on injury prevention, life skills, nutrition; long-term injury surveys; rehabilitation classes; gym programmes scheduled into work time; body conditioning and yoga sessions. However, the major impact of all the work that has been done on dance medicine is currently focused on the areas of dance teacher registration and dance teacher-training, with the raising of awareness now such that Ausdance is having to register 'Safe Dance' as a trademark. Safe Dance is now being incorporated into many school curricula and tertiary dance courses.

Following a pilot study in early 1995, national standards for all teachers of dance in Australia, both vocational and non-vocational, are being developed and include an extensive section on Safe Dance teaching. The draft standards also cover ethical business practice, child development and teaching methodology, but not dance technique, which will continue to be provided by the syllabus organisations.

Some encouraging moves in Britain

In Britain, too, it is beginning to be recognised that a more structured learning programme needs to be introduced to ensure that dance teachers are properly trained, and therefore properly qualified. This is essential to enhance the standing of the profession. As a first step, the Registration Board of the Council for Dance Education and Training have drawn up draft guidelines for in-service dance teacher-training, which are currently being discussed and circulated to appropriate bodies.

Progress in the ballroom dancing field

Until recently, all ballroom dance teacher-training in Britain was also completely technical. With the introduction of the new Disco, Freestyle, Rock 'n' Roll branch, however, the Imperial Society of Teachers of Dancing, one of the major examination bodies, decided to take the opportunity to insist on other subjects being passed as part of the professional teacher qualification. Even at the student level (age 16), the prospective teacher has to be able to show a knowledge of warming up and cooling down appropriate to the style, some awareness of teaching methodology, child development, environmental considerations, basic anatomy and controversial movements. This knowledge is acquired through a mixture of supervised on-the-job teaching and home study. By the time the teacher is aiming for the Fellowship qualification (minimum age 24), he or she would be expected to show how to train other teachers and to have a detailed knowledge of kinesiology, anatomical problems and fitness training. This could well provide a model, suitably adapted, for other bodies offering teaching qualifications.

Towards change

Our study of companies and vocational schools shows willingness to change, sometimes slowly, sometimes more quickly. Even in ideal situations, however, risk and injury remain permanent factors in dancers' lives because of the unique nature of their art. Therefore the need remains for immediate quality treatment. This was the original inspiration for our inquiry. Part of the problem is dancers' reluctance to use it; their desire to continue dancing, their unwillingness to recognise an injury (too often with the collusion of managements), their resort to short-term healing measures, are in themselves career-threatening. At the same time there is much that the dance world can do to reduce the need for treatment. With the whole arts funding system currently operating on standstill resources, healthcare programmes are having to compete with other necessary expenditures and are all too vulnerable to cost-cutting. It will take time for companies and funding bodies to take their responsibilities to dancers seriously, to realise that in the long run this support has to be more cost-effective.

Educational needs

It begins to be clear that any dancers' health and injury service needs to be as much educational as medical. Its provision needs to start in the schools and the companies, with the artistic directors, the principals and with the Boards. It needs to raise awkward questions for discussion. Might it be, for example, that companies' particular methods of work are a cause of injury? Dance UK's conference on training professional dancers provided evidence that unity of training followed through consistently is an important way to counter increased physical demands on dancers. Our work suggests that reducing the injury rate implies questioning traditional training methods, raising fitness levels, asking both managements and dancers to adopt new attitudes. Change on this scale can flow only from the long-term educational measures we propose in chapter 8.

References
1 *Dance UK News* (December 1995), from which case history 4 is extracted
2 Myths dispelled in Tony Geeves' *The Safe Dance Project Report* (The Australian Association for Dance Education (Ausdance), 1990)
3 *South Asian Dance in Schools: A Teacher's Handbook* (Yorkshire, ADiTi, 1995)
4 *The Healthier Dancer* (London, Laban Centre for Movement and Dance, 1991, reprinted 1995)
5 *Opera House*, issue 3 (1994) pp. 56-58
6 *The Classical Ballet Training Study* (Dance/USA 1995)
7 *Tomorrow's Dancers* (London, Laban Centre for Movement and Dance, 1994)

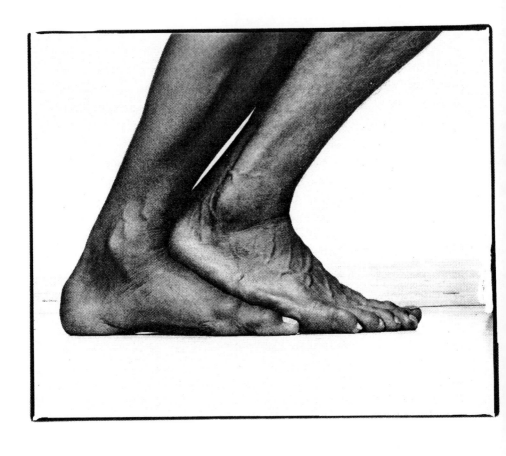

Dancers: Chris Powney/Didy Veldman: Rambert Dance Company
Photograph: Anthony Crickmay

8

The way forward: a review of the chief recommendations arising from the research

THE WAY FORWARD: A REVIEW OF THE CHIEF RECOMMENDATIONS ARISING FROM THE RESEARCH

The recommendations which follow are based on the results of the research commissioned for the Healthier Dancer Programme as well as the other research findings mentioned in the previous chapters. These have been brought to life by the interviews with dance, medicine and science experts. Further refining came from the meetings with representatives from the companies held in September 1995 and with representatives from the vocational schools in February 1996 to discuss some of these findings and recommendations in draft. Those meetings endorsed the work of the Healthier Dancer Programme, believing that it should continue to disseminate information, encourage debate and help to change attitudes.

Time-scale

Some of these recommendations could be implemented fairly quickly, while others are more long-term proposals. Changing attitudes and reviewing teaching methods will certainly take time and will have to be done by gentle persuasion and wider appreciation of the models of good practice. There are roles here for everyone involved in dance, but a critical part must be played by artistic directors, teachers and staff. Dancers' health has to be their prime concern, because without healthy dancers standards cannot be maintained or improved. For many this will mean acknowledging that training methods which worked reasonably well in the past now need to be updated and supplemented with the new information. This may well result in a reassessment of the role of dance teachers; it will take courage, determination and a willingness to learn and to change. The Healthier Dancer Programme work so far has made a convincing case that the dance world is ready to change.

Some of the recommendations which follow obviously apply more to larger companies or training establishments, whereas others apply to smaller ones. Some companies, some individuals, some teaching organisations and some dancers have already implemented many of the recommendations and should take due credit for their progress thus far. Each company, each dancer will have to find an appropriate solution for their particular circumstances. These recommendations are biased towards those which offer the hope of preventing injury, rather than of treating injury once it has occurred, as this is the only long-term way to improve the situation.

RECOMMENDATION 1: DANCERS SHOULD BE PHYSICALLY FITTER

All sports and healthcare practitioners have emphasised the need for dancers to achieve appropriate levels of all-round fitness. Although the physical demands of various forms of dance vary, it is useful to adopt the generally accepted definition of physical fitness as 'the distance between performance requirements and the individual's maximal abilities'. At *The Healthier Dance Conference*, Professor Craig Sharp explained his personal assessment of the levels of fitness demanded in the six areas of cardiovascular endurance, local muscle endurance, muscle strength, muscle speed, flexibility and low percentage of body fat for each of 35 sporting activities; he ranked dance as the second most demanding, behind only gymnastics. Yet the Healthier Dancer Programme research has shown that UK dancers are significantly less fit than dancers in other countries and much less fit than gymnasts.

Flexibility is the dancers' obsession, often at the expense of other fitness components. The dance world embraces, even reinforces, hypermobility, without stressing the extra risks involved and the need to strengthen the muscles around the lax joint. In general, the dance world has been slow to recognise the importance of strengthening as well as stretching and of effective stretching methods.

Dancers resist the advice to strengthen muscles for fear of developing unsightly bulk and losing flexibility. These groundless fears have to be countered by practical experience of appropriate strengthening programmes tailored to the individual dancer.

Although some dancers nowadays, especially in the independent sector, are choosing to incorporate cardiovascular endurance sessions and strengthening activities into their training programmes, there is still a widespread misconception that the standard dance training is sufficient in itself. Yet it is clear that only specifically designed, individually tailored aerobic training will really improve dancers' stamina and thus help to counter those musculoskeletal injuries which are caused by fatigue.

Action points

Companies and schools
- Advise teachers, artistic and rehearsal directors that a fitter dancer will tire less, concentrate better, move faster, and be less likely to get injured, so that dancers are encouraged to commit themselves to a fitness programme.
- Set up fitness assessments to identify individual strengths and weaknesses, in order to devise an individual training programme, with follow-up after a few months to monitor progress.
- Bring in mats and some free weights that properly instructed dancers could use while not required in the studio.
- Make studio space available after class and rehearsal for dancers who wish to do some physical fitness work while their muscles are still warm.
- Make arrangements with local gyms or health clubs or sports centres so that dancers can have access to equipment either free or at a discount.
- Bring in exercise physiologists, physiotherapists and other experts to talk and give practical workshops on aspects of fitness.
- Start the fitness work at the beginning of the season or term and build it into the schedule.
- Enable the individual's fitness profile to be monitored at regular intervals in order to measure progress.
- Make contact with the nearest Pilates technique practitioner and help advertise their services to the dancers; perhaps negotiate special rates.
- Install Pilates equipment and make sure that there are sufficient trained staff to supervise the equipment properly, so that it is available to dancers throughout the day.

Companies
- Tour with a portable Pilates couch.

- Take a set of portable weights or other resistance equipment on tour.
- Insist on new contracts being conditional on a satisfactory physical and physiological examination.

Dancers
- Ask for an individual fitness assessment.
- Find out about local health clubs, swimming pools, Pilates studios.
- Make time available for a proper fitness training programme.

The Healthier Dancer Programme
- Research and advise on an appropriate training programme for dancers in the swimming pool.

CASE HISTORY 8

Christopher Bannerman, previously dancer with London Contemporary Dance Theatre and now Chair of Dance UK; extracts from a talk given at the *Healthier Dancer* conference in September 1990 (reprinted with permission)

'My own dancing life was interrupted by fairly serious back problems. I had ignored warning signs and even to a certain extent had ignored professional advice. Why did I do it and why do others do it? Although this is obviously a deep and complicated matter, (there is) also .. the aftershock of injury - the depression and feelings of being useless and worthless that often come after injury. This is a problem that occurs when the artist's instrument is so closely connected to his own being.

'In my case I could not tie my shoe laces and needed help in dressing. Osteopathy and an intensive course of Pilates-based body control gave me daily goals and a sense of a support system which did wonders for my morale during three difficult months. ... (Upon returning to dance) I made a shocking discovery. I was fitter than I had ever been. I had the flexibility, strength and control to perform all my previous roles without problem and the additional cardiovascular or stamina training I had done meant that I wasn't even out of breath. My attitude to such training programmes changed completely. I had thought that they were cold, soulless and downright boring but necessity was the mother of changed thinking....'

- Research and advise on an appropriate training programme for dancers in a gym setting.
- Research and advise on fitness assessments suitable for dancers.
- Produce a basic booklet on fitness.

RECOMMENDATION 2: DANCERS SHOULD WARM UP AND COOL DOWN PROPERLY

Many dancers say they warm up but, when quizzed more closely, are unable to explain exactly what they are trying to achieve. Many think that warm-up is the same as stretching. Many think that their class is their warm-up, not realising that class is their training and that they need to warm up beforehand. Some still confuse being *warm* when the outside temperature is hot, with being *warmed up*, when the muscle temperature is hot. Some dancers complain of not having space to warm up or of not being given enough notice in rehearsals to warm up before they are needed. Understanding of the need for cool-down is not widespread in dance, but it is particularly important where dancers have been under unaccustomed or undue stress.

Action points

Companies and schools
- Discuss with dancers the places available for warm-up and cool-down to check that they are adequate.
- After discussion with artistic directors, choreographers, rehearsal staff, teachers and dancers, make it policy that dancers are given 5-10 minutes' warning in rehearsal before being required to dance.
- Organise a practical session with a physiotherapist, exercise physiologist or similar expert to teach a dance-related warm-up and cool-down and stress the basic principles.
- Distribute the Dance UK Information Sheet on Warm-Up and Cool-Down.

Dancers
- Make sure they understand the underlying principles of warming up and cooling down.

- Incorporate both into their daily routines until they become second nature.

The Healthier Dancer Programme
- Give practical sessions on warm-up and cool-down.

RECOMMENDATION 3: DANCERS SHOULD EAT AND DRINK PROPERLY

The research shows that dancers are eating too much fat and too little carbohydrate. As people depending on physical activity for their livelihood, they need to keep their carbohydrate intakes high in order to have enough fuel for the muscles, and be more careful to ensure a healthy and balanced diet. Without enough water, the body cannot properly cope with the heat-regulating demands of dancing and the undesirable results include fatigue or muscle spasm. Yet many dancers drink only one or two glasses a day, instead of the generally recommended eight, and worsen the situation by consuming drinks heavily laden with caffeine, such as coffees and colas. Some are more afraid of becoming bloated (a fear which is often unfounded) than of becoming injured through dehydration. Although full-blown alcohol abuse is rare, dancers are not sufficiently aware of its diuretic effects; many, for instance, still think that a glass of wine or beer after a performance will replace the liquid lost during dancing.

Action points

Companies and schools
- Assess the healthy choices available in any on-site catering facilities.
- Insist on healthy food being available at after-show receptions.
- Ensure that all staff know how to recognise the symptoms of eating problems.
- Create a climate that is less obsessed with weight and thinness, more concerned with body composition and shape.
- Bring in experts to talk to the company about nutrition and fluid intake.
- Ensure that there are adequate breaks for refuelling in the schedule.

- Distribute the Dance UK Information Sheet on nutrition.
- Advise teachers of the necessity of adequate hydration.
- Supply water bottles for dancers or encourage them to buy their own.
- Install water fountains in green rooms and other catering facilities.

Dancers

- Make sure they understand why and how they should increase the proportion of carbohydrate in their eating and how they should reduce the proportion of fat.
- Keep the glycogen stores filled for the physical activity required by snacking sensibly through the day and after performance.
- Eat breakfast to replenish depleted energy stores.
- Make sure they understand the importance of keeping the body adequately hydrated.
- Carry water bottles everywhere.
- During high-intensity dancing, remember to take a couple of mouthfuls of water every 20 minutes.

The Healthier Dancer Programme

- Produce a booklet on healthy eating for dancers to supplement the Information Sheet.
- Produce an Information Sheet on eating disorders.
- Produce an Information Sheet on adequate hydration for dancers.

RECOMMENDATION 4: DANCERS SHOULD NOT SMOKE

Even in the Healthier Dancer survey, 36% of the dancers admitted to smoking. Consciously or unconsciously, they may use smoking as an appetite suppressant but would be much better advised to adopt a healthy eating pattern. There are also many other more productive ways of coping with the boredom of hanging around in rehearsal waiting to be called, coping with pre-performance nerves or coming down after a performance, which do not have any detrimental effect on the body and therefore on subsequent performance. The dangers of passive smoking should also be recognised.

Action points

Companies and schools
- Encourage non-smoking areas in all buildings used by dancers.
- Provide counselling for those who wish to quit the habit.
- Bring in experts to talk about the adverse effects of smoking on physical performance and capability.

Dancers
- Stop smoking and encourage other dancers to do likewise.

The Healthier Dancer Programme
- Produce a booklet on the particular dangers of smoking for dancers.

RECOMMENDATION 5: DANCERS SHOULD NEVER HAVE TO WORK IN UNSUITABLE ENVIRONMENTS

One of the major causes of stress fractures is generally agreed to be repeated work on hard surfaces. Unsprung floors also mean undue stress on backs, necks, knees, ankles and feet, which are frequent sites of injury, according to the HDP survey. The risk of catching cold or other viruses for dancers in practice gear or light costumes, sweating heavily after exertion, is greatly exacerbated if the spaces they use are insufficiently heated or badly ventilated.

Action points

Companies and schools
- Ensure that the studios used have properly sprung floors, adequate heating and appropriate ventilation.

Companies
- Educate theatre managers about the implications of these unsuitable conditions for dancers. Plans for refurbishment or redevelopment should then incorporate dancers' needs (reference should be made to the Arts Council of England's book on *Dance Spaces* by Mark Foley).
- Regularly report any inadequacies in touring theatres to the Arts

Council's Touring Department.

- Tour with some carpet offcuts so that dancers do not have to sit or stand on cold concrete in dressing rooms, offstage areas and so on.
- Tour with extra blow heaters.
- Ensure adequate on-stage time for dancers before performances on raked stages.

Dancers

- Refuse to put up with sub-standard conditions.
- Draw the attention of the company or school management or Equity to particularly bad situations.

The Healthier Dancer Programme

- Press for adequate spaces for dance.
- Ensure that appropriate technical and scientific information is available on the subject.
- Investigate the new pointe shoes from America, perhaps with a UK clinical trial.

Funding bodies

- Have audits conducted in their areas of resources such as portable floor systems, linos for hire, studios with properly sprung floors and good ventilation.
- Help to educate theatre managers, boards, other funding bodies and people working in other disciplines.

RECOMMENDATION 6: DANCERS AND TEACHERS SHOULD KNOW MORE ABOUT HOW THE BODY WORKS

'We expect a musician to understand the theory of music but then don't expect a dancer to learn anything about how the body works.' (Sir Peter Wright.) If dancers, teachers, choreographers and artistic directors do not know in detail about how the body functions during movement, they will be unable to understand why a particular movement is less appropriate for the individual. In the long term the aim must be for all students in training to learn anatomy and physiology as applied to dance, but in the meantime many of today's dancers will be tomorrow's teachers and/or choreographers and also need to acquire this knowledge.

Action points

Companies and schools
- Encourage all staff (not just the dancers) to learn some basic anatomy, physiology and kinesiology, especially if they are teaching or may go on to teach.
- Set up screening arrangements for new entrants.

Dancers
- Read appropriate books.
- Take appropriate courses.
- Actively learn from the health professionals they meet.
- Choose teachers who know how the body works.

Teachers
- Encourage their students to use the correct anatomical terms.
- Keep their own anatomical and physiological knowledge up to date.

The Healthier Dancer Programme
- Incorporate aspects of applied anatomy as an essential ingredient of Dance UK information and disseminate this information as widely as possible.

RECOMMENDATION 7: DANCERS SHOULD GET IMMEDIATE TREATMENT FOR INJURY

We have seen that many dance injuries are chronic, and that many become chronic because of late or inappropriate treatment of a minor injury which is allowed to drag on. All health professionals stress the need for early evaluation of symptoms by a dance-experienced practitioner in order to avoid worsening the injury. Problems are difficulty of access to appropriately experienced practitioners and the cost of treatment.

Action points

Companies and schools
- Develop regular arrangements and personal links with experienced health professionals; for example, give them tickets to shows, involve them in regular meetings.
- Have enough physiotherapists available to evaluate and educate as well as to treat.
- Make sure that all appropriate staff know about the Dance UK Medical Register.
- Feed back information on new practitioners to Dance UK.
- Draw up a Health and Safety policy for the organisation.
- Train First-Aiders specifically in dance injuries.
- Keep the First Aid box up to date.
- Keep an injury book, making sure it is up to date.
- Set up systems to keep track of injuries and days off.
- Draw up a healthcare policy for the organisation, involving the Board, senior management, staff and dancers' or students' representatives.
- Set up a regular programme of health education, making use of the contacts and information available at Dance UK where appropriate.
- Designate one person to be the organisation's health representative and encourage them to establish regular communication with Dance UK on the organisation's needs and progress.

Companies
- Take out private medical insurance to cover at least physiotherapy, osteopathy and tests.
- Pay for some medical costs out of company budgets.
- Keep an injured dancer on full basic salary for up to six weeks.

Schools
- Make private medical insurance with appropriate cover available to all students who are not covered by their parents' policies.

Dancers
- Register with a well-informed GP in order to have an initial clinical assessment, access to what is still available on the NHS and referral to appropriate specialist treatment.

The Healthier Dancer Programme
- Investigate the setting-up of a private medical insurance scheme available to all those working in dance.
- Update Dance UK's Medical Register at regular intervals.

Funding bodies
- Make sufficient resources available for all regularly funded companies to pay for dancers' treatments, whether directly or by private medical insurance.

RECOMMENDATION 8: SPECIAL CONSIDERATION SHOULD BE GIVEN TO THE MENSTRUAL STATUS OF FEMALE DANCERS

In parts of the dance world it is considered normal for female dancers to have either very irregular periods (oligomenorrhoea) or prolonged intervals without periods (amenorrhoea). The short-term benefits are lack of period pain and, often, positive reinforcement from peers. But it is now well established that prolonged amenorrhoea as a result of sustained vigorous physical activity is linked to a substantially greater risk of osteoporosis in later life. In the present, amenorrhoea is also implicated in a higher risk of stress fractures, of curvature of the spine and of injuries in general.

Action points

Companies and schools
- Educate staff and dancers on osteoporosis and the dangers of amenorrhoea.
- Educate staff on the high-risk factors for osteoporosis in order to identify those dancers who may be most at risk.
- Be prepared to refer dancers at high risk who have missed periods for at least six months to an endocrinologist or gynaecologist.
- Distribute the Dance UK Information Sheet on osteoporosis.

Female dancers
- Realise the dangerous links between thinness, weakness, poor nutrition and bone health.
- Educate themselves on the risk factors for osteoporosis.
- Realise the importance of a well-balanced eating programme in reducing the risk of osteoporosis and increasing the likelihood of delivering healthy babies.
- Be particularly careful to ensure an adequate intake of calcium, especially in their teens.
- Take sensible, informed decisions on their preferred choice of contraception.
- Encourage their colleagues to keep at least 3-4 periods a year as a minimum.

The Healthier Dancer Programme
- Produce a booklet on the particular health considerations of female dancers.

RECOMMENDATION 9: DANCERS SHOULD KNOW HOW TO RELAX, PACE THEMSELVES, COMBAT STALENESS

Dancers', schools' and dance companies' own regimes of class, rehearsal, training and lifestyles must be carefully planned to aim at preserving fitness and preventing injury. Dr Yiannis Koutedakis has said that if he were in charge of dance in the UK, he would as a matter of urgency have proper rest areas built into every studio and theatre complex in the country so that dancers could take naps or just lie down when not required for work. Dance is sadly lagging behind sport in its appreciation of the importance of scheduling rest and relaxation into any programme of physical activity in order to prevent injury, burn-out and depression of the immune system. In the HDP research, many dancers said that they did not know how to relax, apart from taking a glass of wine and a hot bath.

Action points

Companies and schools should:

- Draw up a plan for the year or the season which includes rest periods as well as work periods.
- Look at the weekly and daily schedules to evaluate the balance between working and resting.
- Look at possible on-site spaces that could be designated as quiet areas, with mats and low lighting.
- Bring in teachers of Alexander Technique, Feldenkrais, t'ai chi, yoga, stress management, transcendental meditation (these could benefit all staff, not just dancers).

Companies

- Discuss with the dancers how conditions in theatres on tour could be improved in order to allow short naps and time out.
- Ensure that rest days on overseas tours really are rest days and not filled with other physical activity or travel, which can be just as tiring.

Dancers

- Increase their knowledge and awareness of the other body therapies.
- Keep at least one day a week free of strenuous physical activity and free of dance.
- Take up a non-dance interest.

The Healthier Dancer Programme

- Produce an Information Sheet on over-training.
- With an exercise physiologist, investigate training schedules suitable for dancers in companies.

RECOMMENDATION 10: DANCERS' PSYCHOLOGICAL NEEDS SHOULD ALWAYS BE CONSIDERED ALONGSIDE THEIR PHYSICAL ONES

Obviously many factors contribute to dancers' estimation of themselves. Companies, teachers, staff and dancers must be aware of the positive effects of good communication and the need to develop a team spirit.

There should be no 'punishing for illness' (Bruce Marks, in interview). Many ballet dancers report that they receive excessive criticism and are not treated as individuals. Counselling and access to sports psychology should be readily available.

Action points

Companies and schools

- Encourage each dancer to draw up a proper career development plan carefully tailored to the dancer's individual skills and potential.
- Encourage teachers to give more positive correction and to be more aware of the effects of their comments.
- Ensure that an injured dancer is kept involved as far as is possible.
- Introduce an appropriate induction programme for newcomers.
- Ensure that proper individual appraisals are carried out annually.
- Set up a link with a dance counsellor.
- Exchange ideas and models of good practice with similar organisations.
- Bring in experts to teach such techniques as visualisation and goal-setting.

Companies

- Ensure that an injured dancer is given the opportunity to contribute to the company as long as mobility permits; for instance helping with teaching, giving talks, taking part in lecture-demonstrations or helping with administrative tasks. This can be viewed as part of the career plan.
- Be inventive about ways of using the experience of dancers who are pregnant or returning from childbirth; this time yields further opportunities for developing skills.
- Keep the dancers informed about the company's policy and future.
- Consider giving dancers unpaid sabbaticals.

Dancers

- Encourage a colleague who wants to talk to someone.
- Make particular efforts to be supportive to an injured or sick colleague.

- Take active responsibility for helping new arrivals as part of an induction programme.
- Become involved in other aspects of dance activity when time permits.
- Take an active role in drawing up a career development plan, seeking appropriate expert advice.
- Develop outside interests.

Teachers

- Remember that each dancer is different and individual.
- Be aware of how much negative and how much positive criticism they are giving, trying wherever possible to emphasise the latter.
- Analyse their own 'performance' with self-correction and goal-setting.

The Healthier Dancer Programme

- Find more counsellors to put on the Medical Register.
- Make links with sports psychologists and feed back information appropriate to dance.

More general points for The Healthier Dancer Programme

- Prepare an annotated list of books on dancers' healthcare.
- Prepare a directory of health-related information for dancers.
- Organise conferences on dance medicine and science, where appropriate with the British Performing Arts Medicine Trust (BPAMT).
- Work with other dance agencies to develop the Dance UK Roadshow programme which disseminates health information.
- Work with the Council for Dance Education and Training on ways to implement recommendations for registered teachers and accredited courses.
- Work with the Foundation for Community Dance on ways to implement recommendations for professional dance artists working in different parts of the community.
- Work on the development of an internationally accepted screening programme for students entering vocational training, which has already been initiated by the International Association for Dance Medicine and Science.

- Investigate the feasibility of establishing dancers' health centres with the aim of bringing together a range of different services with appropriate staffing and facilities, which might include:
  - Fitness assessment and monitoring
  - Fitness programmes
  - Nutritional advice
  - Counselling and occupational psychology
  - Primary care for work-related injury and general health
  - Liaison with specialists for emergency treatment and onward referral
  - Coordination of dance science research
  - Dissemination of information
  - Education and training

Conclusion

It is clear that injuries are caused by many factors, often working in concert. This makes it more difficult to disentangle cause and effect. Difficult, but not impossible. It is also clear that many injuries could be avoided if the dance world as a whole were to adopt some of the basic good practices of the sports world. Although much has already been achieved, - by individual dancers, companies, teachers - there is still much to do, not only in order to prevent dancers' injuries, but also to ensure speedy, appropriate treatment, at little or no cost to the dancer, when they do occur.

It must be remembered that for a professional dancer injury is an **occupational** hazard. Injury costs the dancer dear in terms of time lost, treatment required and possible loss of earnings, and there is an undoubted psychological cost. If the dancer is working in a company, the time lost is the first problem, closely followed by the problems of extra rehearsals and paying for temporary replacements. Not only in order to fulfil their responsibilities as employers, but also in their own best interests, companies must ensure that the dancer has the knowledge and encouragement to take responsibility for his or her own well-being, and that company practices always minimise the risks and maximise the benefits.

Independent dancers have no such division of responsibilities. For them, the assumption of full liability for individual health and well-being is part and parcel of the decision to be a professional dancer. These dancers need help, support and accurate up-to-date facts to enable them to make informed choices in their daily lives and practices.

This has implications for training and for support organisations. While the treatment and management of injury can be improved, the best way forward would certainly appear to be that of prevention. This has to start earlier than the company level. Training establishments have a responsibility to educate as well as to train. If dance is to continue to advance, dancers and teachers need to enhance their technical skills with a range of appropriate knowledge and then to keep up to date. They have to be helped to develop inquiring minds and safe practices.

Change must come. It requires people prepared to be brave, to try new things, to make mistakes and allow others to learn from that experience. It requires resources of time, people, and, above all, money. An investment in dancers' health and injury is required, an investment in the future of dance in Britain.

Appendices

APPENDIX A
THE HEALTHIER DANCER QUESTIONNAIRE

CONFIDENTIAL

Please try to answer all questions; tick the answer or write where appropriate (capitals please). If you do not want to answer any of the questions, please put a cross.

1. What is   a. your gender:
                       Male   ☐
                       Female   ☐
          b. your age group:
                       16-19   ☐
                       20-24   ☐
                       25-29   ☐
                       30-34   ☐
                       35-39   ☐
                       40-44   ☐

2. a. Your height   _____ft _____ins
   b. Your weight   _____st _____lbs

3. Are you currently a. A student   ☐
                      b. A professional dancer ☐

4. Where did you train/are you training now?
   name of school or college _____
   and when? *dates* _____

5. How many years have you been dancing regularly (including school)? _____

6. Is your present dance form
   a.   Classical Ballet   ☐
   b.   Contemporary Dance ☐
   c.   Jazz   ☐
   d.   Tap   ☐
   e.   South Asian   ☐
   f.   Afro/Caribbean   ☐
   g.   Other (please say)   ☐ _____

7. How many classes do you do a week? _____

8. Do you warm up .... ? *Tick as many boxes as appropriate*

	Yes	No	
a. Before class	☐	☐	
b. Before rehearsal	☐	☐	If yes, for how long?
c. Before performance	☐	☐	*Number of minutes* ___

9. Do you warm down .... ? *Tick as many boxes as appropriate*

	Yes	No	
a. After class	☐	☐	
b. After rehearsal	☐	☐	If yes, for how long?
c. After performance	☐	☐	*Number of minutes* ___

10. Have you had any of the following injuries in training, rehearsal and/or performance in the last 12 months? *Tick as many boxes as appropriate*
    - a. Muscular ☐
    - b. Skeleton/bones ☐
    - c. Joints ☐
    - d. Other ☐
    - e. None ☐

11. If you did have injuries, where were the sites of injury?
    Tick as many boxes as appropriate
    - a. Arms/hands ☐
    - b. Shoulders ☐
    - c. Neck ☐
    - d. Upper back ☐
    - e. Lower back ☐
    - f. Ribs ☐
    - g. Pelvis ☐
    - h. Thighs ☐
    - i. Lower legs ☐
    - j. Feet ☐
    - k. Elbows ☐
    - l. Knees ☐
    - m. Ankle ☐

12. How many days have you been unable to work because of injury in the last 12 months?
    - a. 1-3 days ☐
    - b. 4-6 days ☐
    - c. 7-14 days ☐
    - d. 15-21 days ☐

e. More than 21 days ☐
f. None ☐

13. What type of professional help did you have for the injuries?
Tick as many boxes as appropriate
a. Physiotherapist ☐
b. General practitioner ☐
c. Specialist/consultant ☐
d. Masseur ☐
e. Acupuncturist ☐
f. Osteopath ☐
g. Chiropractor ☐
h. Counselling ☐
i. Other (please specify) ☐ _____

14. Who paid for the treatment on the last occasion?
a. Myself ☐
b. Insurance Company ☐
c. Employer/school ☐
d. Shared by employer/school and myself ☐
e. Free on NHS ☐

15. Can you give the rough cost to you of all treatments over the last 12 months?
£ _____

16. What do you think was the cause of these injuries?
please answer for all your injuries and tick as many responses as are applicable
a. Fatigue/overwork ☐
b. Unsuitable floor ☐
c. Cold environment ☐
d. Insufficient warm up ☐
e. Difficult choreography ☐
f. Different choreographers ☐
g. Repetitive movements in rehearsal ☐
h. Partnering work ☐
i. Inadequate diet ☐
j. Psychological (eg depression) ☐
k. Ignoring early warning signs ☐
l. Other (please explain briefly) ☐

17. How do you react to warning signs of an injury?
    a. Tell someone else eg teacher/director ☐
    b. Take own preventative steps ☐
    c. Seek professional treatment ☐
    d. Soldier on ☐

18. How do you tend to phase your recovery after injury?
    a. Take it slowly/follow professional advice ☐
    b. Return as quickly as possible ☐
    c. Follow my own instinct ☐

19. Do you take regular medication?
    a. No ☐   b. Yes ☐
    (If yes, please state briefly what it is for and brand name)
    _____

20. How many years have you smoked/did you smoke? (include all
    smoking periods in between if you have given up more than once)
    Number of years _____-

21. How many cigarettes or ounces of tobacco do you smoke a day?
    a. None ☐
    b. 1-5 ☐
    c. 6-10 ☐
    d. 11-20 ☐
    e. More than 20 ☐

22. How much alcohol do you drink a week?
    in glasses of wine, measures of spirits or half-pints of beer
    a. None ☐
    b. 1-14 ☐
    c. 15-21 ☐
    d. 22-28 ☐
    e. More than 28 ☐

23. If you are currently on a diet, please state briefly what it is:
    _____

24. Have you ever taken advice on diet from:
    a. GP/nurse ☐
    b. Dietician ☐
    c. Magazine ☐

    d. TV programme ☐
    e. Other (please state) ☐ _____

25. What nutritional supplements do you take?
    a. None ☐
    b. Vitamins ☐
    c. Iron ☐
    d. Calcium ☐
    e. Other (please state) ☐ _____

26. Have you experienced any of these in the last 12 months?
    Tick as many boxes as are applicable
    a. General anxiety ☐
    b. Tension with people ☐
    c. Performance anxiety ☐
    d. Depression ☐
    e. Stress due to external factors (eg. bereavement, moving house) ☐
    f. Eating problems ☐
    g. Over-use of alcohol/drugs ☐
    h. General low self-confidence ☐
    i. Sudden drop in self-confidence ☐
    j. Consistent difficulty in concentrating in class/rehearsal ☐

27. How have you started to plan for your retirement from performing?
    a. Consulting Dancers Resettlement Trust ☐
    b. Talking to a counsellor ☐
    c. Following course of study ☐
    d. Developing other practical skills ☐
    e. Planning to have a family ☐
    f. Other (please specify) ☐

28. Have you ever made use of a professional counsellor to talk through personal or professional difficulties?

	Yes	No
a. As a student	☐	☐
b. As a professional dancer	☐	☐

29. If yes, how many sessions did you have?
    a. 1-5 ☐   b. More than 5 ☐

30. Do you have ready access to a counsellor now if you want one?
    a. Yes ☐   b. No ☐

31. If no, would you like to have a counsellor readily available?
    a. Yes ☐   b. No ☐

32. Do you feel that your vocational training prepared/is preparing you adequately for your life as a dancer?
    a. Yes ☐   b. No ☐   c. More or less ☐

33. If not, how could it be/have been better?
    _____

34. In what ways do you think a free or reduced-cost health and injury service for   dancers could best contribute to solving physical and psychological problems?
    _____

Thank you for your time and trouble. We appreciate your help very much.

Copyright © Dance UK 1993

APPENDIX B
THE HEALTHIER DANCER
QUESTIONNAIRE: MANAGEMENTS

CONFIDENTIAL

Please try to answer all questions; tick the answer or write where appropriate (capitals please). If you do not want to answer any of the questions, please put a cross.

1. What is the your company's present dance form?
    a. Classical Ballet ☐
    b. Contemporary Dance ☐
    c. Jazz ☐
    d. Tap ☐
    e. South Asian ☐
    f. Afro/Caribbean ☐
    g. Other (please say) ☐

2. When you are working, how many dancers are there in your company?
    Female *Number* _____ Male *Number* _____

3. How many weeks of employment were you able to offer dancers in the last financial year? *If you work on a seasonal basis, please give total of separate seasons*
    Number of weeks _____

4. Do you keep an accident/injury book?
    a. Yes ☐   b. No ☐

5. How many dance-related injuries have there been in the past financial year?
    a. During class   *Number* _____
    b. During rehearsal   *Number* _____
    c. During performance   *Number* _____

6. How many days have dancers been unavailable for performances due to accident/injury during the past financial year?
    Number ____

7. What are the most frequent sites of injury? *Rank in order of frequency (1=most frequent; 13=least)*
    a. Arms/hands ☐
    b. Shoulders ☐

c. Neck ☐
d. Upper back ☐
e. Lower back ☐
f. Ribs ☐
g. Pelvis ☐
h. Thighs ☐
i. Lower legs ☐
j. Feet ☐
k. Elbows ☐
l. Knees ☐
m. Ankle ☐

8. What range of professional help are you aware is used by the dancers in your organisation? *Rank in order of frequency (1=most frequent; 9=least)*
    a. Physiotherapist ☐
    b. General practitioner ☐
    c. Specialist/consultant ☐
    d. Masseur ☐
    e. Acupuncturist ☐
    f. Osteopath ☐
    g. Chiropractor ☐
    h. Counselling ☐
    i. Other (please specify) ☐

9. Does your company have a regular arrangement with any professional help?
    a. Yes ☐   b. No ☐

    If the answer is Yes, please specify type, number and status:

	Full-time staff	Part-time staff	Referrals
a. Physiotherapist	☐	☐	☐
b. General practitioner	☐	☐	☐
c. Specialist/consultant	☐	☐	☐
d. Masseur	☐	☐	☐
e. Acupuncturist	☐	☐	☐
f. Osteopath	☐	☐	☐
g. Chiropractor	☐	☐	☐
h. Counselling	☐	☐	☐
i. Other (please specify)	☐	☐	☐

10. Who usually pays for the treatment?
    a. Organisation ☐
    b. Insurance Company ☐
    c. Dancer ☐
    d. Shared by organisation and dancer ☐
    e. Free on NHS ☐

11. Can you estimate the cost *to the organisation* of dancers' *treatments* in the last financial year?
    £ _____

12. How many days have dancers been absent from work due to personal or stress-related problems in the last financial year?
    Number _____

13. Which of these problems do you believe are the most frequent?
    Rank in order of frequency (1=most frequent; 8=least)
    a. Emotional pressures ☐
    b. Performance anxiety
    c. Stress due to external factors (eg. bereavement, moving house) ☐
    d. Eating problems ☐
    e. Over-use of alcohol/drugs ☐
    f. General low self-confidence ☐
    g. Sudden drop in self-confidence ☐
    h. Consistent difficulty in concentrating in class/rehearsal ☐

14. How does your company cope with absence due to injury or illness?
    a. Cancel performances ☐
    b. Rehearse other dancers ☐
    c. Take on extra dancers ☐
    d. Other (please specify) ☐

15. Can you estimate in financial terms the cost of absences due to injury or illness? (ie apart from the cost of the treatments)
    £_____

16. Has your company already initiated any health and fitness checks?
    a. Yes ☐   b. No ☐

17. Have you other comments you wish to make, particularly about the prevention or treatment of illness/injury?

18.   In what ways do you think a free or reduced-cost health, fitness
        and injury service for dancers could best contribute to solving
        physical and psychological problems?

        _____

Thank you for your time and trouble. We appreciate your help very much.

© *Dance UK 1993*

APPENDIX C
VOLUNTEERS FOR FITNESS AND NUTRITION TESTING

Male dancers
Andrew Barker
Farooq Chaudhry
Jo Cipolla
Steven Derrick
David Drew
David Fielding
Lee Fisher
Ricardo Goodison
Duncan de Gruchy
Richard Holgate
David King
Tony Louis
Alex New
Toby Norman-Wright
Kevin O'Kane
Peter Ottevanger
Michael Scott

Female dancers
Ishra Ahmed
Caroline Allen
Catherine Andriopolou
Kate Ashby
Amanda Banks
Helen Brennen
Jeannette Brooks
Emma Cater
Andrea Condon
Michelle Davis
Fleur Derbyshire
Dawn Donaldson
Virginia Guy
Nina Hake
Karen Hall
Nicola Hart
Marie-Christine Hobin
Bernadette Iglich
Pamela Johnson

Marie Kjeuberg
Christine Lark
Lee Foon Wong
Kate Legon
Sara Matthews
Siobhan O'Neill
Anna Pakes
Joanna Pegler
Suzanne Preist
Barbara Queirolo
Sophie Richards
Joanna Roberts
Stephanie Ross-Russel
Nikky Smedley
Isabel Tamen
Kirsty Tapp
Seline Thomas
Trine Thomson
Fiona Timms
Julia Todd
Victoria Turner

Male Controls
Christopher Barrio
Mark Grzywacz
Gerald Hayes
John Raynes

Female Controls
Kate Brittain
Jasmine Challis
Joyce Hayes
Magita Khalouha
Sonya Lejeune
Eylath Kranz
Kathy Mills
Anna Molesworth
Joanne Turner
Catherine Willmore

APPENDIX D
THOSE CONSULTED IN THE COURSE
OF THE INQUIRY

In the dance world

Joanne Benjamin, *Michael White Ltd*
Joanna Biggs, *Assistant to the Director, Rambert Dance Company*
Richard Blanco, *Director, Greenwich Dance Agency*
Christopher Bruce, *Artistic Director, Rambert Dance Company*
Deborah Bull, *dancer, The Royal Ballet*
Imogen Claire, *choreographer and Equity Council Member*
Gill Clarke, *choreographer, teacher, dancer*
Sue Danby, *Principal of the College, Royal Academy of Dancing*
Siobhan Davies, *Artistic Director, Siobhan Davies Dance Company*
Janet Eager, *Executive Director, London Contemporary Dance Trust*
Peter Finch, *Assistant General Secretary, British Actors' Equity Association*
Angela Gendall, *dancer, The Royal Ballet*
Malcolm Glanville, *Technical Director, Rambert Dance Company*
Howard Harrison, *Associate Producer, Cameron Mackintosh*
Matthew Hart, *dancer, The Royal Ballet*
Shobana Jeyasingh, *Artistic Director, Shobana Jeyasingh Dance Company*
Mira Kaushik, *Director, Academy of Indian Dance*
Peter Kyle, *Chief Executive, The Scottish Ballet*
Suzanne Lahusen, *Pilates practitioner, Alexander Technique teacher*
Monica Mason, *Assistant Director, The Royal Ballet*
Maryanne McNamara, *Administrator, Phoenix Dance Company*
Margaret Morris, *Artistic Director, Phoenix Dance Company*
Mark Murphy, *Artistic Director, V-Tol*
Lloyd Newson, *Artistic Director, DV8*
Siobhan O'Neill, *Artistic Director, Chisenhale Dance Space*
Douglas Pringle, *Touring Manager, The Scottish Ballet*
Derek Purnell, *Administrative Director, the Birmingham Royal Ballet*
Piali Ray, *Director, SAMPAD*
Simon Rice, *dancer*
Anthony Russell-Roberts, *Administrative Director, The Royal Ballet*
Petra Siniawski, *choreographer, dancer*
Mark Skipper, *Company Manager, Northern Ballet Theatre*
Tania Slayter, *Production Administrator, Really Useful Company*
Peggy Spencer, *Teacher; Fellow and Examiner, Imperial Society of Teachers of Dancing*
Ann Stannard, *Principal, Central School of Ballet*
Britt Tajet Foxell, *Psychologist, The Royal Ballet*
David Williams *Head of Administration/Personnel, English National Ballet*
Linda Yates, *Administrator, Dance Companies Resettlement Fund and Dancers' Resettlement Trust*

In the dance and medicine world

Lesley Ackland, *remedial exercise consultant, Body Maintenance*
Janet Briggs, *physiotherapist, Royal Ballet School*
Julia Buckroyd, *psychotherapist, counsellor*
Simon Costain, *podiatric consultant, The Gait and Posture Centre*
Susie Dinan, *exercise therapist*
Shirley Hancock, *physiotherapist, RDC Physiotherapy Clinic*
Alan Herdman, *Pilates-based exercise specialist*
Justin Howse, *orthopaedic consultant; Chair, British Association of Performing Arts Medicine*
Aileen Kelly, *Chief Physiotherapist, The Royal Ballet*
Christine Lister, *osteopath*
Caroline Marsh, *physiotherapist*
Warrick McNeill, *physiotherapist, Physioworks*
Paul Morrisey, *osteopath*
Peter Norman, *podiatrist, The Montagu Clinic*
Dreas Reyneke, *The Body Conditioning Studio*
Alex Scott, *Administrator, British Performing Arts Medicine Trust*
Elizabeth Sharp, *physiotherapist*
John Strachan, *orthopaedic consultant*
Islay Sullivan, *physiotherapist, the Birmingham Royal Ballet*
Mark Sylvester, *physiotherapist, Physioworks*
Roger Wolman, *Consultant in Sports Medicine, Royal National Orthopaedic Hospital*

In the sports and medicine world

John Atkinson, *Technical Director, British Amateur Gymnastics Association*
Dr Roslyn Carbon, *Department of Sports Medicine, Royal London Hospital*
Celia Carron, *Director, Aquarobics Teacher Training*
Peta David, *Press Officer, Central Council of Physical Recreation*
Richard Godfrey, *physiologist, British Olympic Medical Centre*
Jane Griffin, *nutritionist/dietician, British Olympic Association*
Vivian Grisogono, *physiotherapist, Royal Masonic Hospital*
John King, *Chairman, British Association of Sport and Medicine; orthopaedic consultant, Department of Sports Medicine, Royal London Hospital Medical College*
Nancy Laurenson, *Education Officer, British Association of Sport and Medicine*
Rose MacDonald, *Director, Crystal Palace Sports Injury Centre*
Professor Greg McLatchie, *Director, National Sports Medicine Institute of the UK*
Lesley Mowbray, *Head of Training & Development, London Central YMCA*

Wrio Russell, *Co-director, London School of Sports Massage*
Barry Simmonds, *London Regional Development Officer, National Coaching Foundation*
Dr Dan Tunstall Pedoe, *Medical Director, London Marathon*
J G P Williams, *orthopaedic specialist in injury rehabilitation*
Dr Jane Wilson, *Medical Registrar, British Olympic Medical Centre*

Researchers
Dr Ann Bowling, *Reader in Health Services research, Centre for Health Informatics and Multi-Professional Education, University College of London Medical School*
Dr Nicola Keay, *Research Fellow, Guy's and St Thomas's Hospitals*
Magita Khalouha, *research student in nutrition, University of London*
Caroline Kitchin, *podiatrist*
Matthew Wyon, *research student in exercise physiology*

Overseas
Barry Brownstein, *physiotherapist, SOAR Physical Therapy Center, New York City*
Julie Dyson, *National Executive Officer, Ausdance*
Tony Geeves, *dance teacher, researcher, Australia*
Elizabeth Larkam, *Director, Dance Medicine Division, St Francis Memorial Hospital, San Francisco*
Marijeanne Liederbach, *Coordinator, Harkness Center for Dance Injuries, New York City*
David McNamara, *dance fitness therapist, Nederlands Dans Theater*
Marika Molnar, *physiotherapist, Westside Dance Physical Therapy, New York City*
Craig Phillips, *physiotherapist, Dance Medicine Australia*
Eva Ramel, *physiotherapist, Sweden*
Dr Wendy Reiser, *family physician, Toronto, Canada*
Boni Rietveld, *orthopaedic consultant, Nederlands Dans Theater*
Margot Rijven, *Amsterdam School of Arts*
Donald Rose, *Director, Harkness Center for Dance Injuries, New York City*
Joysanne Sidimus, *Executive Director, Dancer Transition Centre, Canada*
Itzhak Siev-Ner, *orthopaedic specialist; Director, The Israel Dance Medicine Center*
David Weiss, *orthopaedic specialist, New York City*
Helena Wulff, *psychologist, Sweden*

APPENDIX E
FURTHER READING

Books

ARNHEIM, Daniel D, *Dance Injuries: their prevention and care* (Princeton, NJ, Princeton Book Company, 1986, 3rd edn 1991)

BEAN, Anita and WELLINGTON, Peggy (eds), *Sports Nutrition for Women* (A&C Black, 1995)

BERARDI, Gigi, *Finding balance: fitness and training for a lifetime in dance* (Princeton, NJ, Princeton Book Company, 1991)

BLAKEY, Paul, *The Muscle Book* (Bibliotek Books, 1992)

BLAKEY, Paul, *Stretching Without Pain* (Bibliotek Books, 1996)

BUCKROYD, Julia, *Anorexia and Bulimia* (Element Books, 1996)

BUCKROYD, Julia, *Eating Your Heart Out* (Optima, 1989, reprinted 1994)

CALAIS-GERMAIN, Blondine, *Anatomy of Movement* (Seattle, Eastland Press, 1993)

CHMELAR, Robin D and FITT, Sally S, *Diet: A Complete Guide to Nutrition and Weight Control*, (Princeton, NJ, Princeton Book Company, 1990)

CLARKSON, Priscilla M and SKRINAR, Margaret (eds), *Science of Dance Training*, (Human Kinetics Books, 1988)

FITT, Sally Sevey, *Dance Kinesiology* (Macmillan, 1988)

GRAY, Judith, *Dance instruction: science applied to the art of movement* (Human Kinetics Books, 1989)

GRIEG, Valerie, *Inside Ballet Technique – Separating Anatomical Fact from Fiction in the Ballet Class* (Princeton, NJ, Princeton Book Company, 1994)

GRISOGONO, Vivian, *Sports Injuries – A Self-Help Guide* (John Murray, 1984)

GRISOGONO, Vivian, *Children And Sport – Fitness, Injuries And Diet* (John Murray, 1991)

HOROSKO, Marian and KUPERSMITH, Judith, *The Dancers' Survival Manual* (Harper & Row, 1987)

HOWSE, Justin and HANCOCK, Shirley, *Dance Technique and Injury Prevention* (A&C Black, 1988, 2nd edn 1992)

MAFFULLI, Nicola (ed), *Colour Atlas and Text of Sports Medicine in Childhood and Adolescence* (Mosby-Wolfe, 1995)

NORRIS, Christopher M, *Flexibility: Principles & Practice* (A&C Black, 1994)

OLSEN, Andrea, *Body Stories: a guide to experiential anatomy* (Station Hill, 1991)

PEARL, Kenny, *Dance Life*, (Toronto, Dancer Transition Centre, 1990, reprinted 1993)

RYAN, Allan J and STEPHENS, Robert E, (eds), *Dance Medicine: a comprehensive guide* (Pluribus Press Inc, 1987)

RYAN, Allan J and STEPHENS, Robert E, (eds) *The Healthy Dancer: Dance Medicine for Dancers,* abridged (Dance Books in association with Princeton Books, 1989)

RYAN, Allan J and STEPHENS, Robert E, *The Dancer's Complete Guide to Health Care and a Long Career* (Bonus Books, 1988)

SHARKEY, Brian J, *Physiology of Fitness* (Human Kinetics Books, 1979, 3rd edn 1990)

SHELL, Caroline G, *The Dancer As Athlete: The 1984 Olympic Scientific Congress Proceedings, vol. 8* (Human Kinetics, 1986)

SOLOMON, Ruth; MINTON, Sandra C; SOLOMON, John, (eds), *Preventing dance injuries: an interdisciplinary perspective* (American Alliance for Health, Physical Education, Recreation and Dance, 1990)

SOLOMON, Ruth and SOLOMON, John, (compilers) *Dance Medicine and Science Bibliography* (Andover, NJ, J Michael Ryan Publishing, 1996)

SPILKEN, Terry L, *The Dancer's Foot Book,* (Princeton, NJ, Princeton Book Company, 1990)

STIRK, John L, *Structural Fitness* (Elm Tree Books, 1988)

SWIEGARD, Lulu, *Human Movement Potential, its ideokinetic facilitation* (Harper & Row, 1987)

THOMPSON, Ken, *The Movement Book* (Bibliotek Books, 1996)

VINCENT, L M, *The Dancer's Book of Health,* (Princeton, NJ, Princeton Book Company, 1978, reprinted 1988)

WATKINS, Andrea and CLARKSON, Priscilla M, *Dancing longer, dancing stronger: a dancer's guide to improving technique and preventing injury* (Princeton, NJ, Princeton Book Company, 1990)

WHITE, David R, FRIEDMAN, Lise and LEVINSON, Tia Tibbits (eds), *Poor Dancer's Almanac,* (Duke University Press, 1993)

WILMORE, J and COSTILL, D, *Physiology of Sport and Exercise* (Human Kinetics Books, 1994)

WIRHED, Rolf, *Athletic Ability and The Anatomy of Motion* (Wolfe Medical Publications, 1984, reprinted Mosby-Wolfe, 1995)

Journals

Dance Magazine
Editor: Richard Philip
Monthly magazine published by Roslyne Paige Stern
Available from Dance Books, 9 Cecil Court, London WC2N 4EZ

Dancing Times
Editor: Mary Clarke
Monthly magazine published by Dancing Times Ltd,
45-47 Clerkenwell Green, London EC1R 0EB
E-mail: dt@dancing-times.co.uk

Impulse: The International Journal of Dance Science, Medicine, Education
Editor: Luke Kahlich
Quarterly with research articles and academic reviews on dance and dance-related issues
(last issue summer 1996)

Journal of Dance Medicine and Science
Editors-in-Chief: Karen Clippinger, Scott Brown
Quarterly with research articles focusing on the identification, treatment, rehabilitation and prevention of illness and injuries in dancers
(first issue autumn 1996)
Available on subscription from J Michael Ryan Publishing,
24 Crescent Drive North, Andover, New Jersey 07821, USA
Tel: +1 973 786 7777 Fax: +1 973 786 7776

Medical Problems of Performing Artists
Editor: Alice Brandfonbrener
Quarterly journal of the Performing Arts Medicine Association
Published by Hanley & Belfuss, Medical Publishers,
210 S 13th Street, Philadelphia PA 19107, USA

Performing Arts Medicine News
Quarterly journal of the British Association for Performing Arts Medicine
Available from The British Performing Arts Medicine Trust,
196 Shaftesbury Avenue, London WC2H 8JL

APPENDIX F
USEFUL ADDRESSES

UK

Dance

Academy of South Indian Dance
in the UK
Hampstead Town Hall
213 Haverstock Hill
London NW3 4QP
Tel: 020 7691 3210
E-mail: admin@akademi.co.uk

Arts Council of England
14 Great Peter Street
London SW1P 3NQ
Tel: 020 7333 0100
Fax: 020 7973 6590
E-mail: inquiries@artscouncil.org.uk

Arts Council of Wales
Cyngor y Celfyddydau Cymru
9 Museum Place
Cardiff CF10 3NX
Tel: 029 2037 6500
Fax: 029 2022 1447
E-mail:
information@ccc-acw.org.uk

British Actors' Equity Association
Guild House
Upper St Martin's Lane
London WC2 9EG
Tel: 020 7379 6000
Fax: 020 7379 7001
E-mail: info@equity.org.uk

Council for Dance Education and
Training (CDET)
Studio 8
The Glasshouse
49a Goldhawk Road
London W12 8QP
Tel: 020 7746 0076
Fax: 020 8746 1937

Dance UK
Battersea Arts Centre
Lavender Hill
London SW11 5TF
Tel: 020 7228 4990
Fax: 020 7223 0074
E-mail: danceuk@easynet.co.uk

Scottish Arts Council
12 Manor Place
Edinburgh EH3 7DD
Tel: 0131 226 6051
Fax: 0131 225 9833
E-mail: administrator@
scottisharts.org.uk

Dance and Medicine

British Performing Arts Medicine
Trust (BPAMT)
196 Shaftesbury Avenue
London WC2H 8JL
Tel: 020 7240 3331
Fax: 020 7240 3335
E-mail: bpamt@dial.pipex.com

Sport and Medicine

Association of Chartered
Physiotherapists in Sports
Medicine (ACPSM)
c/o 58 Rathmore Road
London SE7 7QN
Tel: 020 7377 7846

British Association of Sport and
Exercise Sciences (BASES)
114 Cardigan Road
Leeds LS6 3BJ
Tel: 0113 230 7558

British Association of Sport and
  Medicine (BASM)
c/o Birch Lea
67 Springfield Lane
Eccleston
St Helens WA10 5HB
Tel & Fax: 01744 28198

British Olympic Association
  (BOA)
1 Wandsworth Plain
London SW18 1EH
Tel: 020 8871 2677
Fax: 020 8871 9104
Website: www.olympics.org.uk

British Olympic Medical Centre
  (BOMC)
Northwick Park Hospital
Watford Road
Harrow
Middlesex HA1 3UJ
Tel: 020 8864 0609/3135
Fax: 020 8864 8738

Central Council of Physical
  Recreation (CCPR)
Francis House
Francis Street
London SW1P 1DE
Tel: 020 7828 3163
Fax: 020 7630 8820
E-mail: admin@ccpr.org.uk

Crystal Palace Sports Injury
  Centre
Jubilee Stand
Crystal Palace National Sports
  Centre
London SE19 2BB
Tel: 020 8778 9050
Fax: 020 8659 1501

The Exercise Association
Unit 4, Angel Gate
326 City Road
London EC1V 2PT
Tel: 020 7278 0811
Fax: 020 7278 0726

London Central YMCA
112 Great Russell Street
London WC1B 3NQ
Tel: 020 7343 1700
Fax: 020 7631 5101

National Coaching Foundation
  (NCF)
114 Cardigan Road
Headingley
Leeds LS6 3BJ
Tel: 0113 274 4802
Fax: 0113 275 5019
E-mail: coaching@ncf.org.uk

National Osteoporosis Society
PO Box 10
Radstock
Bath BA3 3YB
Tel: 01761 471771
Fax: 01761 471104
E-mail: info@nos.org.uk

National Sports Medicine
  Institute of the UK (NSMI)
c/o Medical College of St
  Bartholomew's Hospital
Charterhouse Square
London EC1M 6BQ
Tel: 020 7251 0583
Fax: 020 7251 0774
E-mail: info@nsmi.org.uk

Sport England
16 Upper Woburn Place
London WC1H 0QP
Tel: 020 7273 1500
Fax: 020 7383 5740
Website:
www.english.sports.gov.uk

Sports Nutrition Foundation
National Sports Medicine
    Institute of the UK (NSMI)
c/o Medical College of St
    Bartholomew's Hospital
Charterhouse Square
London EC1M 6BQ
Tel: 020 7250 0583
Fax: 020 7251 0774
E-mail: info@nsmi.org.uk

Books, Videos

Coachwise
114 Cardigan Road
Headingley
Leeds LS6 3BJ
Tel: 0113 231 1310
Fax: 0113 231 9606
E-mail:
    inquiries@coachwise.ltd.uk

Dance Books
15 Cecil Court
London WC2N 4EZ
Tel: 020 7836 2314
Fax: 020 7497 0473
E-mail: dl@dancebooks.co.uk

Libraries

Centre for Sports Science and
    History
Main Library

University of Birmingham
Edgbaston B15 2TT
Tel: 0121 414 5843
Fax: 0121 471 4691
E-mail: censsah@bham.ac.uk

National Resource Centre for
    Dance (NRCD)
University of Surrey
Guildford
Surrey GU2 5XH
Tel: 01483 259316
Fax: 01483 259500
E-mail: nrcd@surrey.ac.uk

National Sports Medicine
    Institute of the UK (NSMI)
c/o Medical College of St
    Bartholomew's Hospital
Charterhouse Square
London EC1M 6BQ
Tel: 020 7251 0583
Fax: 020 7251 0774
E-mail: info@nsmi.org.uk

Sport England
16 Upper Woburn Place
London WC1H 0QP
Tel: 020 7273 1500
Fax: 020 7383 5740
Website:
    www.english.sports.gov.uk

OVERSEAS

Australia

Ausdance Inc
PO Box 45
Braddon ACT 2612
Australia
Tel: +61 6 248 8992
Fax: +61 6 247 4701

Dance Medicine Australia
10 Cecil Place
Prahran VIC 3181
Australia
Tel: + 61 3 9525 1566
Fax: +61 3 9525 1263
E-mail: dancemed@ozemail.com.au

Canada

Dancer Transition Centre
66 Gerrard Street East, Suite 202
Toronto
Ontario M5B 1G3
Canada
Tel: +1 416 595 5655
Fax: +1 416 595 0009

Holland

The Foundation for Dancers'
  Health
c/o Netherlands Theatre Institute
Herengracht 168
Postbox 19304
1000 GH Amsterdam
Netherlands
Tel: +31 20 625 64 24
Fax: +31 20 620 00 51

West End Clinic
Lijnbaan 32
Postbox 432
2501 CK The Hague
Netherlands
Tel: +31 70 330 2056
Fax: +31 70 380 9459

Israel

The Israel Dance Medicine Center
19 Cremieux Street
Tel Aviv 64259
Israel

Tel: +972 3 685 4706/ 685 8734
Fax: +972 3 685 3641

United States of America

Dance Medicine Division
St Francis Memorial Hospital
900 Hyde Street
San Francisco CA 94109
USA
Tel: +1 415 353 6400
Fax: +1 415 353 6401

Harkness Center for Dance
  Injuries
Hospital for Joint Diseases
301 E 17th Street
New York NY 10003
USA
Tel: +1 212 598 6022
Fax: +1 212 598 7613

International Association for
  Dance Medicine and Science
  (IADMS)
c/o Jan Dunn MS
2555 Andrew Drive
Superior CO 80027
USA
Tel: +1 303 554 8040
E-mail: iadms@aol.com

Performing Arts Medicine
  Association (PAMA)
c/o Dr Ralph Manchester
250 Crittenden Blvd Box 617
Rochester NY 14642-8617
USA
Tel: +1 303 751 2770
Website: www.artsmed.org